Courage After Coma:

A Family's Journey

by Mufty Mathewson

First Printing June 1997
Second Printing Aug 1997
Third Printing Apr 1998
Fourth Printing Nov 1999
Fifth Printing Dec 2004
Sixth Printing Feb 2007

Published and distributed by:
Uneek Experience Ltd.
10333-132 Street
Edmonton, AB. Canada
T5N 1Y9

Canadian Cataloguing in Publication Data
Mathewson, Mufty, 1933-
Courage After Coma

ISBN 0-9682221-0-2

1. Mathewson, Wendy, 2. Brain damage--Patients--Canada--
Biography. 3. Brain damage--Patients--Rehabiliatation--Canada.
4. Brain damage--Patients--Family Relationships. I. Title
RC387.5.M3 1997   362.1'97481'092   C97-910466-1

"What Survivors of Brain Injury Want You To Know" reprinted by permission of The Perspectives Network, TPN Inc., PO Box 1859, Cumming GA 30128

Editor-in-chief & graphic designer: Gerry Boudrias
Photography: Mufty Mathewson
                                        Front cover photo: Gerry Boudrias

This book is dedicated
with love and admiration to
Wendy,
the most courageous daughter
anyone could ever have.

Acknowledgments

Many people are responsible for this book and to all I give heartfelt gratitude. Just as people arrived to help with Wendy's recovery when we needed it most, so too, people have turned up to help with this book when I needed it most. They are those who believed it was important, those who encouraged, those who read the manuscript in any of its many forms, and those who gave ideas and suggestions. It never would have happened without them. The mistakes in the book are mine.

Major driving forces were; Ronna Jevne, who made me believe I could do it; Muriel Scott, fellow artist, Sharon and Sheryl Rohr and their friend Eileen Bekius, who have travelled a similar path; Barbara Turner-Vasselego, teacher of freefall writing; Ruth Bertelsen, Courtney Milne, Sherrill Miller, Franny Hall, Diana Tremain, Rob Graesser and Steve Truch who read and commented. Cecile Gillett and Barb Downes, detail experts; Elaine Downes, computer coach; Barb and Dwight York, who have stood by Wendy, Nancy Brine, Elaine Roberts, and Mairead Kehoe who made valuable suggestions. Finally thanks to wizard editor Gerry Boudrias, whose knowledge of minutiae and ideas of book design were so freely and generously given.

Thanks are due to my family members who have read it, cried again, and given me their memories of how they saw what happened. I thank Bruce, Michele, Bob, Shelley, and Doug. I thank Bill who has read every page many times and read much of it to Wendy many times. He has encouraged, supported and loved me. He is an incredible life-partner who makes me better than I am. This book is part of our healing. Now it is time to send it forth to inspire others who need courage.

Contents

Foreword

Every parent has experienced their son or daughter becoming ill or getting injured and needing support and nurturing. The need to protect, love and support a son or daughter is as natural as giving birth. Some parents have also experienced the incredible feeling of helplessness that comes from being totally unable to assist their child through the illness or injury. Mufty Mathewson describes what every parent feels, or would feel, if their daughter was injured like Wendy. Her description of living with the news of the accident, the coma, the initial recovery, the vicissitudes of life after brain injury is poignant and gut wrenching.

I have had the opportunity to interview hundreds of families living with the effects of an acquired brain injury as part of my research on the topic. Each's family's story is unique. Here, there are common elements that many families face when living with the effects of acquired brain injury. I am sure that most families would appreciate knowing about these common elements early after the injury. Families want to know what they may face and how other families have coped. This book will be a tremendous help. This book will also help families that have endured the changes, as the Mathewsons have. These families will cry with Mufty and Wendy and they will laugh with them as well. The stories are true to life and articulately described.

Mufty describes the events of the years since Wendy's auto crash, in simple, yet descriptive terms. You admire the strength of the family as they cope with the effects. You understand the reactions the family has to the return of an adult daughter to a childlike, dependent state. You cheer for them as Wendy takes giant steps toward self determination. You admire Wendy's courage and Mufty's love. The book will fill a need for everyone living with the effects of serious injury to a loved one. It is written in such a readable fashion that everyone can enjoy it and learn from the Mathewsons.

Barry Willer, Ph. D. is a Professor in the Department of Psychiatry and Rehabilitation Medicine at the State University of New York at Buffalo. He is an adjunct Professor at Brock University, in St. Catharines, Ontario. Dr. Willer is a board member of his local head injury association (Fort Erie) and the national organization (Canadian Brain Injury Coalition). In 1997 he served as interim Director of the Ontario Brain Injury Association. Dr. Willer has published widely on brain injury and the effects on the family. He has lectured extensively on the topic of acquired brain injury and has offered courses on brain injury rehabilitation in four different countries.

Preface

On November 30, 1987, on a dark, cold night, the phone call every parent dreads came to us. Wendy, our twenty-seven year old daughter, was in a car accident. Something shattered her skull and crashed into her brain. Wendy lay in a coma for six weeks. Her physical recovery from coma and paralysis took months but her ability to speak, to write her thoughts, and to read, is her ongoing life's work.

With a child's computer game, repeating words, again and again, she began her relearning. She pursued years of speech therapy, spent over $25,000 for aphasia programs, relearning centres, brain injury programs and rehabilitation centres. With her indomitable will, she, a University graduate, has struggled to regain her vocabulary, one word at a time. Her fierce and ongoing labour for independence has earned her the admiration and respect of family, friends and acquaintances. She searches to find a new place in society where she can feel important and useful. Her search is one which I, her mother, have watched with pride, incredulity, sorrow and wonderment. She is succeeding!

Wendy is ambivalent about my writing of her recovery. She does not like being the subject of a book although she feels the story needs to be told. But who wants her mother to write her own story? It is painful for Wendy, as she knows that she cannot write it herself. She once loved to write; long letters and University papers. Now there is a connection missing. She cannot do it. Yet!

This is not just her story. It is our family's story too. The stories are different. Throughout Wendy's recovery I kept a journal. I recorded her triumphs and her struggles. But I cannot know them all. More accurately I recorded my own version of her recovery from the worst event of our lives.

I searched for other stories of people recovering from brain injury but could find none until 1990 when I found *For The Love of Mel,* by Edna Lissett Hunter of The Association for the Rehabilitation of the Brain Injured, (ARBI) in Calgary, Alberta. It is an incredible story of Mel's long struggle back from massive brain injury. It was difficult reading. Much of his pain and struggle and his mother's ache and anguish acutely matched my own, but it gave me great hope.

Last night I opened the dusty cardboard box where the tired pink files are stored, documenting seven years of Wendy's life. The legal files alone are ten inches thick, two for each year in preparation for the law suit which followed the car accident. Rereading the details of what we have been through exhausts me. There are release of information forms for all the health professionals she saw: case co-ordinators, doctors, occupational therapists, psychologists, neuropsychologists, neurologists, physiotherapists, and speech therapists. There are forms and duplicate forms for Assured Income for the Severely Handicapped and for disability pensions, along with letters, dental reports, CAT scan reports, MRI scans, medications, seizure reports, places of residence, aphasia schools, bills, and bank loans.

I've got to be out of my mind to want to tell this story. Perhaps the reason there are so few stories about people who are recovering from brain injury is the sheer exhaustion of the survivors and their families.

I tell my version of Wendy's journey as honestly as I can. My challenge is to record our ongoing, daily, uphill struggle in a positive way. Wendy lost her life work as she knew it, her companion of eight years, her life style, her income and her independence. Her daily battle is to make sense of those losses. We are full of admiration for her.

Wendy's accident has changed our family. We have new respect for what is important, so it is the family story too. And a mother's story. We trust that it will give hope and courage to others.

Chapter 1

Terror

I wake terrified.

I am instantly alert, searching for the source of the terror. Bill is beside me, gently snoring. The curtains are drawn, windows secure. Where is the terror coming from?

Wendy! Wendy. In the hospital! That's where it is coming from. Wendy is in trouble! I know it as surely as I have ever known anything. I must get to her. She's in danger.

I throw on yesterday's clothes, grab my runners, my coat, the car keys and hurry down the steps to the garage. The car is warm, ready to go on this five o'clock, dark winter morning. I back out pressing the electric door as I speed off up the street.

Hurtling along the curves, I become one with the car, accelerating swiftly, weaving, lighter than a car, to quicken my way to Wendy's side. I drive into a metered place by the door. To hell with quarters. Her life is more important than money.

I wait for the elevator, bursting with impatience. I race onto her ward, wild to remember where they put her yesterday when they took her out of intensive care.

I remember thinking, she isn't ready to leave intensive care.

Not yet! They're moving her because they need the bed, not because she is ready. They are moving her because she was the least critical of the critical patients. I am used to the warmth and the security of the nurses station eight feet from Wendy's bed. These are excellent nurses. I am used to the gurgling sounds of respirators, bleeping sounds of monitors, noisy snuffles of suctionings. Nurses monitoring living hearts under brilliant lights. There were gaspings, moanings, and groanings, but there were also nurses right there.

Asexual nurses, swathed in blue paper caps, masks, gowns, tied baggily about the waist, paper shoes soundlessly gliding across floors responding to the life-ebbing clues of monitors. These nurses had kept Wendy alive. They knew her with her white-bandaged head, splinted leg, swollen, blackened eyes. The crisis care nurses in intensive care knew how we loved her and needed her back.

But the nurses in this new ward don't know Wendy at all. She was only moved here yesterday. She is too far from the desk!

As I rush into the ward I see no one at the desk. I dash at Wendy's room, bash open the door and see her, lying askew, head off the pillow, wedged between the bed railing and the mattress. Her tracheotomy tube is gurgling, wheezing, blocked, unblocked, blocked. Wendy has no air. There is just the wet, moist smell of sputum caught in the plastic tube in her throat. Her left hand is weakly pulling at her ventilator.

I stand, terrified, knowing I cannot lift her. But it doesn't matter. I walk confidently to the far side of the bed, throw my purse off my shoulder, car keys flying out with a clink. I slide my hands, backs flat, hard-down against the rough sheet, under her limp warm body; I curl my fingers upward and heave with the might of a warrior woman, hauling her across to me, her mother. Across to my breast. Across to my warmth and strength so that she will not suffocate.

Air rushes into her lungs. I fall on her chest, my chest to her chest, holding her. Warm. Soft. Hearing her breath, clearer now, gurgle past the open tube, past the trachea, past the bronchi, past the bronchioles, into the little sacs known as alveoli, the tiny cavities where oxygen exchanges with carbon dioxide in the blood to travel back to the heart to be pushed to the brain to say, it's OK now. We have air again. We have oxygen now. We're OK. We live.

I lie shaking, half on the bed, flooded with relief. I have saved Wendy. I know now why I woke. I reaffirm our psychic connections.

Slowly fury fills me. Where are the nurses? When had they checked her last? Why the hell did they take her out of intensive care?

I look up and a smiling, young nurse comes into the room. She knows nothing of this drama. She has come in by chance. I tell her my tale. She is concerned and asks why I didn't ring for a nurse. I have no answer. I didn't think of it. There was no time. Only need for action.

It's not important now. What seems essential is to get Wendy out of that bed. I ask for a wheelchair, a reclining wheel chair and for help to get Wendy into it. Suddenly several nurses are there, all helping, solicitous, soothing me, suctioning her trach tube, cleaning her up, wiping away the mucous smeared on her throat, making her comfortable in a reclining wheelchair.

I am focused on the sunrise. I have to see the sunrise and I must show it to Wendy. She is still semi-comatose, but somehow, I know she and I must see the sunrise, mother and daughter together.

I know where East is, so I push the heavy, unwieldy chair, past the elevators, down the quiet hall towards the East. There is a large red and black sign which says HEMATOLOGY, DO NOT ENTER. I bang open the doors with the foot of the chair. It is a large room with several green-topped islands at which hematologists work. At this early Sunday hour all the stations are empty except one. A slight dark young woman looks up over her test tubes filled with patients' blood.

Beyond her there are long windows to the east. I push the chair up to the window. The sky is streaked with purple, rose, scarlet, crimson and coral, the colours we need back in Wendy's cheeks. And red. The colour of blood; of life, of strength, of vitality, of energy.

I whisper in her ear. "Wendy. Wendy, I have brought you to see the sunrise. We needed to see the sunrise, you and I. See Wendy. Isn't it gorgeous?"

She lies inertly on the pillow, eyes closed. She is resting. I look up and watch the yellow globe that is the sun, rim the horizon, slowly grow larger, become a crescent, become a half, become a whole with warm rays cutting through the winter's cold, searing itself on my retina. I stand a long while beside Wendy, her cheek against my cheek, willing her to see the sun, knowing that she will again and that I will again and that we will keep on fighting this thing together until she is well.

Then I take her back to the ward and leave her with the new nurses who now know more about Wendy. I go home to my warm bed, grateful that I can cry again with Bill.

Chapter 2

A Special Child

Every child has a singular place in a mother's heart. When I was a young woman, for no reason I can remember, I firmly believed that I would be the mother only of sons. That was fine with me. I grew up with two terrific brothers and thought that having sons would be great.

Bill Mathewson and I met at McGill University in Montreal. We had a seven year, on-again, off-again courtship and finally married in 1957. We had an adventurous, six-week, hitch-hiking honeymoon in Europe where we spent all our savings and then moved west to Calgary, Alberta to begin our married life. Bill was starting a career as an investment dealer and I, as a physiotherapist. We had the world by the tail.

Our first born was Bruce, in 1958, a perfect blue-eyed baby boy; my destiny, mother of sons, coming to pass. When I became pregnant again, expecting on May 19th of 1960, I assumed it would be a brother for 1 1/2 year old Bruce.

On May 24, I was awakened at 5 a.m. by a vivid dream in which dice were being cast. There were four black dice and one white. The black dice kept winning. I was somewhat upset by the dream but turned my huge belly over and went back to sleep. Later that morning, I saw Bill driving our little tan coloured Volkswagen hastily back along our street.

I wondered what he had forgotten. He came into the house, sat me down on the stairs just inside the door and put his arm around me.

He said, "Mufty, your father died this morning. They gave him the anaesthetic for his heart surgery and he died before they could begin."

I was desolate. My father and I were soul mates. We were alike, thought alike and shared a sense of humour and a huge interest in other people. We accepted one another with unconditional love. Now he was dead. We had known his chances of surviving the surgery were only twenty percent. I remembered my morning dream and realized that with the time zone change, I had dreamed it when he died. The black dice had won.

I longed to go to Dad's funeral in Montreal, but instead, stayed in Calgary, with Bill, waiting for the birth of our baby. I was sure my emotional loss would bring on the baby, but the day of the funeral, I waited for signs of labour and none came. "This baby is not going to share the limelight with anyone," said a friend, "it's going to come in its own time when your mourning is over." And so it was. Finally, more than two weeks overdue, on June 4, the baby was born.

The doctor said, "It's a girl!" I couldn't believe it. A girl baby! A girl. A warm tender ecstasy flowed through me. I went quite berserk, laughing and crying with joy. I was jubilant! I wept and yelled and was absolutely delirious with happiness. I felt particularly clever presenting Bill with a daughter, hoping their relationship would be as close as Dad's and mine had been.

We named her Wendy Susan. Wendy for the joy of the name and Sue, the nickname my father fondly used for me. In the years that followed we had two more boys. Bob, our blue-eyed dark- haired baby, in 1962 and Doug, our very blond, adorable youngest in 1965.

Wendy was a happy, easy baby, bright and quick, fun to be with right from the beginning. All the children were. I watched for signs of sibling rivalry but it just didn't seem to exist in our young family. It hadn't happened with Bruce when I brought Wendy home and it never seemed to happen with the others either. They were generous in accepting and enjoying one another. With four children born that close together our days were busy and good with bright happy children. We loved life and we loved one another.

I was a mostly stay-at-home mother, but periodically practiced physiotherapy on a part-time basis. Sometimes I treated private patients in their homes or taught prenatal classes in my home. I loved practicing my profession and I loved being a wife and mother.

Although I had always had a bad back, shortly after Bobby was born, it became a very serious problem. Bobby was a colicky baby which added to the challenge. Picking him up was agony. Bending over to pull on children's shoes, wash children's faces or pick up toys or clothes was very painful. Although Wendy was only little at that time, she was always helpful.

Finally, a spinal fusion was inevitable. My six months of hospitalization and recovery was a hard time for us all. It was difficult keeping someone in a household with three children under five and a mother recovering from a not-too-successful back surgery. We had a series of thirteen different women coming in to do child care and housework. I was still unable to do any of the work and felt inadequate as we went further and further into debt.

Bruce, our eldest, took extra energy. A charming, smiling, dreaming, hyperactive child, he had great difficulty in school. He was totally honest, and so precious, but would argue endlessly about why he couldn't do his homework, be home on time, follow directions or help around the house. A diagnosis of a learning disability (later dyslexia) explained his behaviour but there was no help for it then.

Wendy was always a willing helper. She was good to her little brothers. She was the organizer. Even as a very little girl she would plan car trips, make lists and devise activities for the kids in the back seat.

In school she excelled. Tall for her age and strong, she was good at sports. She showed skill and talent with horses early in life. When she was eight she went to Elkana Ranch camp in Bragg Creek, Alberta. She amazed us with her confidence around big horses. She pushed them around and let them know she was boss.

We had a good life in Calgary. Watching the six Mathewsons leave the house to go to the Calgary Stampede, ten gallon white hats, cowboy shirts and string ties for the boys, squaw dresses for the gals, was a noisy, fun, rowdy event. We whooped and hollered, whistled and waved, never self-conscious about having fun.

In 1969 Bill accepted the position of Manager of Dominion Securities, in Edmonton, Alberta, two hundred miles north of Calgary. The move was hard for some of us, but Wendy adapted quickly and made many friends. A real little water rat, she became involved in competitive swimming. A growing collection of ribbons told the tale of her success. She was remarkably independent. If I was unable to drive her, she rode her bicycle to early morning practices. On bitter winter days, she walked, coming home with her blond braids frozen from the cold, but determined to be there and to give it her all.

Wanting her own money, Wendy started her first job when she was thirteen, washing cars. Her early teenage years were turbulent with a peer group that worried me and her dad. We managed to keep the communication channels open. We knew we were on the right track when she chose to confide in me, when a dreadful gang rape happened in her circle of friends.

She had a mentor in her Junior High music teacher, Brian

Appleby. He spent time talking with Wendy and pushed her to work hard at her music and to see the value in pursuing excellence playing in both the Grade and Concert Bands.

Wendy was always sensible. When struggling through her grade ten at Ross Sheppard High School, doing only adequately, she realistically worried that she would fail. She came to us and said, "I'm afraid I am not going to make it if I stay at school here. You'd better send me away." Fortunately, her Granny was able to finance boarding school, so the following two years, she attended Balmoral Hall in Winnipeg, Manitoba, where she made great friends and excelled both scholastically and personally. At her graduation she won the Rosemary G. Condo Memorial Award, a special prize for a girl who is kind and gentle, caring for others. She played her flute to accompany the choir in the "Brother James Air" in the graduation ceremonies. We were proud and thought the award was perfect for Wendy.

Although Wendy was always attractive, outgoing, interested and concerned about other people, she was truly modest and unpretentious, like her father. She was generous in praise and compliments for others.

Like many young high school graduates, Wendy wasn't sure what she wanted to do with her life. She knew she wanted to be out of doors and she knew she wanted to make the same money as her brothers and male friends. She studied Surveying, then Agriculture and then travelled with a friend to Australia and New Zealand. Finally she found her niche at the University of Alberta in Recreation Administration. She graduated in 1985 with a Bachelor's Degree.

Throughout her schooling, she jumped at job opportunities that presented themselves. One, was being an interim flight attendant with Wardair, a regional chartered airline, which was threatened with a strike. The training, compressed into a two week course, was in Florida. The strike did indeed happen so Wardair used the quick trainees to keep the flights in the air. During her few weeks with them she flew to Germany, Hawaii, London and Holland. She realized that a flight attendant's job was that of a waitress in the sky which she didn't like at all.

During her teen years Wendy always had lots of boy friends, a couple more serious than others. Most were not romantic relationships. They tended to be pals. Good pals. She never lost her head over boys. She just enjoyed their company and they enjoyed her.

In 1979 Wendy met Tom Kehoe. She was nineteen. He was twenty-two, tall, good looking with soft curly hair and an easy grin. Not long after Wendy met Tom, she came into the kitchen one day while I was making supper. "Mum," she said, "I've met this guy and he's really nice. He comes from a family just like ours." It was true. Ann and Jim Kehoe were warm and friendly people who opened their home and hearts to all their children's friends and stray pets. Wendy enjoyed them all, forming fast friendships with both sisters, Lydia and Mairead, and liking Tom's three brothers, Jim, Dan, and Sean as well. Wendy and Tom were a couple for the next eight years.

Every New Year's Day the Kehoe's rented a rink for a family hockey game. Friends and family, whether two or sixty-two, laced up skates, formed into teams and played a traditional game. As soon as Wendy came into Tom's life, all the Mathewsons were included in the Kehoe family events and they in ours.

Tom was truly an outdoorsman, making his living by guiding, taking people on hunting and fishing trips to camps in remote areas of northern British Columbia and Alberta. A man of few words, he preferred listening, or silence, to chatting.

He and Wendy hunted together. She had become a good shot. When the children were about twelve, they began hunting with their dad and "Grampie," Bill's dad, for upland game. We often had duck, partridge and pheasant to eat in the fall. When Grampie died in 1986 he left Wendy his hunting shotgun.

After University, Wendy had several jobs in the recreation field. She was a recreation therapist at Alberta Hospital, the Lynnwood and Grandview Auxiliary hospitals.

In 1985, she started her own business called "Uneek Experience", which organized expeditions during which people could experience the wilderness. Her first tour was to British Columbia to view the great Adams River Salmon Run. Her bus load of forty-six people had an educational adventure, picnicking in historic places, watching the spawning salmon with naturalists leading their lessons at the site. People were anxious to go on the next "Uneek Experience" with Wendy.

She loved being out-of-doors, so decided to spend a summer working in northern B.C. with Tom. They had an adventurous summer and fall together and when it was over decided to commit to living together at last. They found a little cabin on Lac Ste. Anne west of Edmonton, and Wendy set about finding a new job in recreation while she planned more Uneek Experiences. We were happy that Wendy was so well on her way to a wonderful life.

On November 30, 1987 she and Tom were heading home, travelling west from Edmonton, in Wendy's small car. They had five frozen turkeys in the back, gifts for their families for Christmas.

Tom was driving. In the dark, he saw a car swerve on the highway ahead. He slowed in time to see a deer lying on the road. Beside it, a man was out on the roadside examining his headlights. There were no flashers on so Tom drove around the deer, beyond the car and pulled over to the shoulder where he started to back up so that they could help pull the deer off the road.

A Camaro, driven by Eva Stelter, also going west, travelling fast, hit the deer, soared into the air, then came down, slamming into the back of Wendy's car, driving it sixty feet up the bank.

Both Tom and Wendy were unconscious when Eva looked into their car. A passing motorist with a radio phone reported the accident immediately to the Royal Canadian Mounted Police. (R.C.M.P.) Ambulances were there in minutes. They got Tom out first from the driver's seat and then carefully got Wendy out. A frozen turkey was found at her feet. Her skull was crashed and dented on its left side. We later suppose she may have turned around to look as they were backing up. Possibly the collision drove the frozen turkey, like a projected cannon ball, into the left side of Wendy's head. We will never know.

A seven-minute ambulance ride took them to Stony Plain Hospital near Edmonton. Possibly because of her abundant hair, her head injury was not detected in that initial assessment. They presumed a broken neck but the crushed skull on the left side went unnoticed. They knew it was very serious so sent her immediately to the University of Alberta Hospital in Edmonton, sirens howling in the dark winter night.

Chapter 3

November 30, 1987

The call comes from the Royal Canadian Mounted Police, Spruce Grove Detachment.

"Your daughter has been in an accident. It is very serious. We are sending her to the University Hospital in Edmonton. Go there right away. We think she has a broken neck. Tom Kehoe was in the accident too. He is not seriously hurt. We have called his parents."

Numb, we hurl ourselves into our car and speed to the University Hospital. Bill drives while my mind races. I say, "We must be assertive. We will say, we need to be with her. If she is going to die, Elizabeth Kübler-Ross, expert on death and dying, says we need to be with her, so we have to focus on ... we need to be with her."

Wendy is not in the emergency ward when we arrive. The nurse tells us she is at x-ray and suggests we wait in a special room. She calls a pastor. I am furious. What better way to tell us Wendy is dying! I determine not to speak to him. He is a comfort to Bill, but I stay detached. I repeat to the nurse. "We need to be with her."

After an interminable fifteen minutes Wendy returns from x-ray. We are called to a small, aseptic cubicle where she lies still on a stretcher. A nurse is holding a black bag which has a short tube attached to Wendy's mouth. She is squeezing and releasing it, in and out, in and out, breathing for Wendy. Our beautiful twenty-seven year old daughter, gorgeous masses of blond hair in disarray, eyes swollen and shut, mouth full of the breathing tube, blood seeping from her ear, lies inert. Light is brilliant in the room, but it is all too clear that Wendy is unresponsive. No, it is deeper than that. She is simply not present in the room.

I take a Kleenex and gently dab at the pinkish fluid dribbling from her left ear. The nurse says gently, "Please don't do that."

"Why?" I ask, incredulous. She says in a matter of fact voice, "We need to measure how much brain fluid she is losing".

And so we stand beside our daughter, helpless, while a nurse compresses and releases the black bag breathing for Wendy. It makes soft whooshing sounds. I am grateful for the nurse's sureness, her calm, her endurance. Squeeze, release; squeeze, release; squeeze, release.

We stand, waiting for the surgeon who will take the smashed skull bones off her brain. Otherwise the swelling in the confined space of her skull will kill her. It isn't very long before a green clad orderly comes to take her away. The nurse goes beside her, squeezing, releasing, squeezing, releasing the black bag.

There is nothing we can do. Nothing!

Reality begins to seep in. The reality of how close to death Wendy is. I say to Bill, "Let's go home. It's not going to do us any good being here for eight hours. I can't sit. We have a long, long road ahead of us. I need to go home and lie down now. We are only twelve minutes away from the hospital."

And so we do. We go home to rest.

We hold each other. We talk about the possibility of her death. We decide that we will release her organs for donation. We fall asleep.

At four o'clock I wake. Whack goes my brain. Wendy! I slip

into the den and phone directly to the operating room. They tell me they have just sent Wendy down to the Intensive Care Unit (ICU).

The University of Alberta Hospital is newly renovated. It is light, open, airy, full of windows, atria and green growing plants. But the waiting room outside the Neurosurgery Intensive Care Unit, 4A4, is in a dark corner of the hospital, with ugly, slippery, cold, green vinyl chairs, lined up four feet across from a wall, facing a closed door. A yellow, plastic phone receiver hangs on the wall by the door. A sign reads: VISITORS AND RELATIVES PLEASE DIAL 57 BEFORE ENTERING.

We do.

An impersonal voice says, "Who do you wish to see?" "Mr. and Mrs. Mathewson for Wendy." we say. "We're cleaning her up," they say. "It will be about ten minutes." The speaker goes dead.

We sit holding hands in the green, vinyl chairs under the dim harsh greenish light of neon bulbs. We are touching each other but our brains are coping independently. What will she look like? Will we be able to handle what she looks like? Will there be tubes and bottles and blood? Will she be cut and maimed?

After an eon, the speaker crackles to life and says, "Wendy is ready now." We leap to our feet and push slowly through the door to the unforgiving brilliant light of intensive care. She is there in the first bed, right in front of us, lying high up like a sarcophagus. We stand together on the same side of the high, cold, chrome, pulled-up sides of the hospital bed and look at our daughter.

Her head rests on a pillow swathed in a huge white bandage which almost covers her eyes. They are puffy and swollen shut, tinged with blue. There is a tube in her nose. There are wires coming out from under the bandage attached to a machine which is bleeping by my right ear. She is wearing a black, blood pressure cuff. It expands and collapses regularly. The white sheet, folded over a white blanket, comes tidily under her chin. Underneath, I can see that she is catheterized with a tube attached to a bottle under the bed. But the sheet and cover are neatly positioned under her chin and her arms are under the sheets. I reach under and bring out her left hand. I hold it. Squeeze it gently. Hold it tenderly. It is warm and just the right size. This is Wendy. The rest is not. There is no life to the face. No response. No animation. No life. No movement. No smile. No eyes. Just a mask with big swollen eyes with black smudges under closed swollen lids. Unresponsive. In a coma. This is what "in a coma" means.

She is close to death. Later we learn that she was a 3 on the Glasgow Coma Scale of 1 to 10, a common tool to measure the depth of coma. 3 is close to death.

We stand there looking.

We say, quietly, "Hi."

"Hi Wendy."

"It's Mum and Dad, Wendy."

"We're here."

"We love you Wen."

"You're going to get better Wendy."

We look at the machines and wonder what they mean. What do they monitor? What are they doing for Wendy? What are they telling us? How can we learn what they say?

A kind, attentive nurse explains. That machine measures the pressure in her brain. If it gets dangerously high, it means the swelling will do more brain damage or it could be the cause of Wendy's death. We watch that one very carefully as though watching will make a difference. This one is breathing for her. Her chest rises and falls slowly, mechanically. The other machines monitor her temperature, her blood pressure, her electrolytes, her blood gases. I look at the nurse and think how considerate she is of us, how pretty, how young. I cannot take in any more of what she is saying. She must realize we are unable to concentrate any longer and she slips away, leaving us alone.

We look at the machines. The numbers mean nothing. We read the name on the machine. It is a BEAR machine. We think this is a good omen. Wendy's dog's name is BEAR. We grasp at the straw that BEAR is in here with her, looking after her. That feels good.

We look back to Wendy. No change. No movement. Nothing. Still swollen face under the bandage cloche. Still, closed eyes. Still, fresh, white sheets unmoved. Still breathing machine, chest rising evenly, up and down, up and down.

"Hi, Wendy." we say, louder now. Not so intimidated.

"We love you, Wendy."

"Tom's OK, Wendy". "He's in St. Albert" we shout, wanting to get through the coma. Through the unresponsiveness.

"Hi, Wendy. We need you back here, darling. Please come back. We need you here." I squeeze her hand.

She lies still. There is no movement behind her swollen lids. No response. No answer. No reaction. We are learning what coma means.

The nurse materializes beside us to say the resident doctor can speak to us now. We will learn what this head injury means. What this cruel label "brain damage" means. He tells us that Wendy's situation is very serious. He shows us a CAT scan, representative x-ray slices of Wendy's brain, some areas dark, black in the eerie green light of the x-ray viewing box. Black on the left side of her brain, but on the other side, the right side, it is not black. The brain scan shows no skull, no white where they have removed the bone. The amount of skull removed is the size of a small saucer. He points out the damage in the temporal and parietal lobes and says there is unknown damage to her brain stem too. He tells us that the areas most seriously damaged control speech, memory, and comprehension. He tells us that she has youth on her side. We nod as though we understand, but what can we know about what that means? Speech, memory and comprehension. We say nothing. Yes, we nod numbly, as though we understand.

From home, Bill and I phone Wendy's brothers. We phone the Kehoes. They have taken Tom back to the hospital, semi-conscious. He has also been hit on the head and has hurt his back. He has two terrible black eyes. He is admitted to St. Albert Hospital for observation.

We phone Wendy's friends. We tell our friends. We ask for their prayers. There is nothing else to be done. Whether the prayers go to Gods or Goddesses, Allah, the Great Spirit doesn't matter. We need it all.

Journal Entry: December 5, 1987
On December 1, the world stopped for us.
sorrow,
     sorrow,
          sorrow,
               sorrow,
                    sorrow.
anguish, tears.
Wendy lies, being breathed for, her beautiful hair under a bandage,
her skull crashed in.
She is Brain Damaged.
What a hideous label
     Brain damaged.
          Brain damaged.

Chapter 4
Joyful Prayer Service

Wendy lies motionless and unresponsive in Intensive Care. On the first Sunday, 6 days after the accident, we feel there should be some kind of service. None of us are church goers, but there is a sense that a gathering, focusing on the positive, will be helpful. We try to hold it in the McMullan Gallery at the hospital, a lovely space dedicated to art and music, donated by a friend of ours, Lori McMullan in memory of her late husband, Bill. However the authorities think that it will set a precedent and refuse us the use of the space. Our daughter-in-law, Bruce's wife, Michele says, "Why do you have a living room with a cathedral ceiling, if not to use it?" So we tell friends who call that there will be a "Positive Prayer Service for Wendy" at our house at one o'clock on Sunday. They are asked to bring candles. Later, we count 64 people who come despite such short notice.

My best friend, calm and thoughtful Elaine Roberts, is in Ontario practicing physiotherapy. We have been friends since the year our two daughters were 13. We sent them away to camp together and since then, her Diane and our Wendy have been close. Diane has studied many alternate methods of healing and asks if she can lead a Visualization for the service. Gratefully, I say, "Of course." The room fills with treasured friends. It is a large warm room with a long picture window overlooking the snowy cold buried garden and beyond to the trees of a ravine. Inside there is a welcoming, circular stone fire place with a gentle, genial, wood fire burning.

People sit in and on the arms of chairs, on the rug and spill over into the kitchen. It is Tom's first time out since the accident and he comes with his parents. He sits silently on the floor with his mother nearby. He is very quiet. Diane sits on the stone fireplace while she leads us in a joyful visualization. She sees Wendy standing near a fountain, or possibly a waterfall. She is well, smiling and greeting and knowing each of us.

Jim Kehoe, Tom's Dad comes in from the hospital. He is jubilant at what he has seen and shares his joy with us. He tells us that Wendy was lying, spread-eagled all over the bed when he visited her at noon. He called out to her in his lovely Irish brogue, saying, "Hello my darlin' huntin' partner". Her leg and her hand flew up and she opened an eye to look at him. He is so excited and thrilled that his Irish enthusiasm fills the room. We all cheer and laugh and cry at this first sign of response.

Then we all sing songs for Wendy. Two friends have hastily put together a song book called "Songs For Wendy" which we sing, accompanied by guitar. I stand and thank people for coming and tell of my realization that Wendy is taking us all on the ultimate Uneek Experience.

Then Bruce, Wendy's kind, caring, older brother, 6'5" tall, gets slowly to his feet. He says, "In the previous five days I have heard many people say, "If anybody can get over this terrible accident, Wendy can. She's just that kind of a person. We are asking a lot of Wendy. I feel we should all work on ourselves, so that we can be strong for Wendy." He pulls two red, satin ribbons out of his pocket, divides us into two groups and gives each group a red ribbon. He asks that one group go down the ravine behind the house and the other to Alexander Circle Park on the next street. Each group is to put their ribbon as high up in a tree as possible, so that it will brighten the scenery and represent Wendy looking at us. Then during the dark winter ahead we will look up, not down, as we walk, thinking of Wendy.

Everyone gets to their feet, puts on their coats and scarves and gratefully lights candles and sparklers. Our two groups leave the house on that cold, winter afternoon, taking a little light into the darkness of the outdoors. In one group, Diane's boyfriend, a forester, climbs a tall green spruce in the Ramsay Ravine. In the other, a child climbs on Bill's shoulders to put the ribbon high on a naked elm tree in the park. People wander back to the house where food magically appears. Bill and I go together to the hospital after this wonderful service, remembering that Diane saw her smiling and greeting people. Wendy lies still and unresponsive in intensive care.

This becomes our Hope Ritual. Each time we walk around the neighbourhood, we look up, thinking of Wendy.

Journal Entry: December 7, 1987
I am calmer.
Exhausted, stronger,
weaker.
> *Visualizing Wendy in a pink room, full of sunshine and hope.*

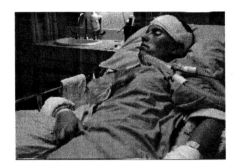

Chapter 5

Intensive Care

Our focus is to be positive. Whatever happens will be for the best. We do not want to hear negatives. We imagine the best. We visualize good things happening for Wendy. We need to get the swelling and waste products out of her head. We visualize the blood of her body carrying away the bruised blood in her head. The damaged areas need new, clean circulation. We will make it happen by all concentrating on what is needed.

Our friends, Tom's friends, Wendy's friends, our family and Tom's family all respond. People begin to congregate at our house. We support one another. We organize the times each of us will go up to the hospital to be with Wendy. "Just family," say the nurses in intensive care. We put Bruce, Bob, and Doug on the family list. We put Diane on the list. We put Tom's two sisters, Mairead and Lydia, on the list. We put Tom on the list. Even though he is still in the St. Albert Hospital, we put him on the list. We keep putting people on the list of "family" because we know Wendy needs them all.

Bob, our tall, dark, bearded, deep-thinking, son, has read that the most primitive sense to return, when people come out of a coma, is that of smell. He and Doug, the blond, easy- going, hockey-playing, artist brother, bake a batch of fresh bread. They time it so that it will be ready just when the ICU doors open for visiting time. Together they take a hot loaf out of the oven and jump into the car and drive quickly to the hospital, rush up to intensive care, break open the bread and waft it under Wendy's nose. They say, "Hey, Wendy, wake up. Smell this bread? If you don't wake up, your brothers will eat it! Wake up, Wendy. Wake up!"

She doesn't wake up. She doesn't respond.

Friends put together a package of smells from their kitchens of spices and herbs. They shop for peppermint, roses and lemon. They take their aromatherapy to Wendy. They put it under her nose with words. "Come on Wendy, wake up!" But it doesn't work. She is unable to respond.

Diane asks me if she can work energy fields on Wendy. I agree, but say I haven't enough strength to explain what she does to the doctor. Diane says, "No problem. I will do it". When the doctor learns that she will not touch Wendy, he grants his permission. Diane places her hands in Wendy's energy fields above her body. She shapes and moves the energy. The nurses watch, ask questions and Diane finishes and leaves. It feels good to be able to do something.

Diane says it would help to put some colour on Wendy to counteract the blood and swelling in her head. We put a soft blue satin bow on her bandage to counterbalance the red in Wendy's brain. Diane suggests something yellow on Wendy's chest to help her heart. We find a great florist bow, as yellow as butter, and pin it to her hospital gown.

I feel that Wendy's appearance is so unlike her, so remote, so impersonal, that I want some way for the nurses to know about this special, remarkable young woman, far away in her coma. Perhaps if they can see who she really is, they will respond to her more warmly. I remember a photo I had taken recently of Wendy talking on the phone. I take it down to the film lab where I have an account for my business, Fayre Photography. They know Wendy and they are shocked that she has had such a terrible accident. They enlarge the photograph at once, put it on foam core and give it to me without charge. I know that vibrant Wendy. I drive the picture to the hospital feeling that I shouldn't be driving. I can't concentrate on traffic. Every time I think of what is happening to Wendy I am so profoundly sad that I cry. I tack the photograph on the wall above her bed in Intensive Care so that everyone will know the real Wendy. I tell the nurses that she is hearing everything they say on the phone in the picture, so to look at it and tell her wonderful, affirming things.

The nurses are great. They talk to Wendy, kindly, gently, enthusiastically. They tell her what they are going to do before they do it. They talk to her when they read the myriad of numbers blinking on the machines, when they check on her, when they take her blood pressure or turn her over. They like the picture. They say they are glad to know what she really looks like. I am reassured. I feel I have done something positive.

Journal Entry: December 8, 1987
HOPE! Wendy went up to the Operating Room to have the brain probe, measuring intra-cranial pressure, and a tracheotomy done. Now, she is to be sedated for two to five days with no stimulation.
Last evening her great white cloche bandage was gone as was the cruel white tape plastered to her upper lip, keeping the tubes in place. Her tracheotomy was in place and quite bloody. Her hair had been cut. There was just a white bandage around her head. I made another blue bow on a safety pin, through my tears and put it on the bandage. It was lovely to see her face and ears again.

As a physiotherapist I learned my neuroanatomy thirty-seven years ago. I know that recovering from a brain injury is a long and difficult process. I know that sometimes people stay in a coma for years, curling into a fetal position, responding not at all to outside stimuli. I remember as a student treating a young woman, first in 1952, and then four years later when I was teaching at McGill. She was still there in the same bed, curled tighter into her fetal position, hands clenched, elbows permanently bent, knees flexed to her chest. Gracie, in a coma for five years, safe for students to learn handling techniques on. Could she still be there? I wonder how her mother felt, watching her, year after year in a coma?

I remember other patients that inch back to consciousness, slowly learning to move one muscle, one joint, one limb at a time. How do we know what will happen to Wendy? I am terrified that her recovery will be so slow that we will not be able to see the changes. I also know that we will need markers to know that there are changes and to know that she is recovering. I need to see it. I need to be able to measure it.

I am a photographer now, a visual kind of person. I need to record what I see. My business is to make slide shows. My subjects are often social issues, like the decision unwed mums have of whether or not to keep their babies; about grieving; about people with disabilities.

I think that if we have photographs of Wendy's recovery; early ones, we will have tangible evidence of her progress. I remember that I am scheduled to speak at the annual conference of the National Association of Photographic Art (NAPA) in Regina, in July. My subject is "Health and Healing in Photography." Intuitively, I understand that this is why I am working on this project at this time. Somehow a slide show about health and healing will help Wendy and me, and possibly others with their healing. I know I need to photograph her recovery. Finally, a direction for my energy.

I rest in the ante room outside Intensive Care, thinking about this, trying to gain enough strength to photograph Wendy; the unresponsiveness, the stillness of her coma. I know that bringing a camera into a hospital is against hospital policy. At that precise moment Wendy's neurosurgeon, Dr. Peter Allen, comes past the room, alone. I call to him and tell him of my decision to photograph Wendy's recovery. He thinks it is a great plan. He gives me his permission, but says that I must clear it with Administration and with the head nurse in ICU.

I go straight down to the Administration office to ask someone with authority for permission. They too, are totally supportive, saying that they would be greatly interested in seeing the finished product when it is done. Relief! All that remains is the head nurse.

I go back to Intensive Care. I tell her what I want to do. She flatly refuses. Her reason is that Wendy is an adult in her care. She cannot allow me to invade the privacy of one of her patients by photographing her. As well, she is afraid that I might photograph some of the other patients.

I am astonished. I swear I will not photograph any of the other patients. I tell her that I have the approval of both Dr. Allen and of Administration, that they both think it is a good idea and they support my project. She waivers. She is in charge of Wendy's best interests and does not want me to take pictures. I am dumbfounded by her refusal but remain determined. I tell her that I am losing my ability to convince. I ask her to please, just think about it. I visit with Wendy.

I sit quietly by Wendy's bed, watching the Bear respirator evenly pushing air into her lungs, expanding her chest up and out, then releasing, so that it sinks to rest. The numbers blinking on the digital readouts are within what we now know are good numbers, her intracranial pressure is stable, her heart-rate strong, her temperature within the bounds of normal. I rest my head on her bed, holding her hand, and will her to get better.

"If anyone can do it, Wen," I say to her, "you can".

"You have always been such a fighter, such a fabulous daughter, Wen, that if anyone can fight their way out of this mess, you can."

"I'll be here," I say to her, "with whatever skills I can bring, with all my energy, with all the strength that a mother can fight with, I'll help you, Wendy."

"I love you so much Wendy and I want you back."

"I need to take your picture Wendy. Wouldn't that be a great idea! How come this authoritative head nurse needs to exert her power to stop me from doing what I know you would support and would enjoy as a project", I tell her.

"Wen, you are one of my biggest photography fans." "I told the nurse, Wen, that you would approve."

"I told her that you also are a great photographer. But I guess it's in the lap of the gods, Wen. Just keep fighting, daughter of mine, just keep fighting and I'll fight too."

I visualize the blood coursing strongly through her brain, racing through the arteries, carrying away more waste products of the accident, healing the axons and dendrites of each cell. Each time I cross the North Saskatchewan River, on my way to the hospital, I think of the force and strength of rivers coursing mightily under the ice in the winter. I use this image to keep the blood flowing in Wendy's brain, lessening the bruising and eliminating the waste products of the insult. I see her blood flowing as strongly as the strong, powerful, unending current of that great river. I visualize a great, red pump with a thundering sound to increase the flow of her blood to heal the brain tissue under the bandages. I pour energy from my body into her body. I become calm. I stand up to leave. I go over to the head nurse to ask her for her decision. She tells me I may photograph Wendy. I thank her and head home to rest, to find my camera to record the incredible journey ahead.

Chapter 6

The Telephone Answering Machine

Our days begin to find a rhythm. Our dependable, daughter-in-law, Michele, comes over each morning. Ever the untiring mother, she brings our grandchildren Kyle, 4, and Kory, 6 months. She stays with me and answers the phone, makes coffee, and cleans up the kitchen. The one phone call I can't take is from Eva Stelter, the woman who drove the car that hit Wendy and Tom. She phones one morning to say how sorry she is. She is my age and has children the same ages as ours. I am unable to talk to her. I am so grateful Michele is there.

We settle into a routine of hospital visiting. When I am home I wander aimlessly around the house, feeling a weight in my head, in my chest, in my heart. I cry. I talk. I laugh. I make time to meditate each morning trying to calm myself. I walk each day. I pour all my misery into my journal. I am grateful to talk to people who phone or who drop in. The kindness people demonstrate is amazing. They think of things to do before we know what we want. What I do know is that this event will be a long, long time in resolution. I will be unable to do it alone. I decide that I will accept all the help that is offered. I will need it all. I feel grateful for it all.

The phone seems to never stop ringing. The calls are essential to us, but we have little energy to return them. We have a new telephone answering machine so, each day, we put an update of Wendy's progress on the machine. People soon understand they will not be troubling us and will be getting the latest information about Wendy by phoning.

When we get home from the hospital we are renewed and revived by the many messages of love, hope, help and prayers. We have no phone calls to make. We never feel alone or abandoned. There are friends wanting and needing to help as close as our telephone machine.

The messages we leave on our telephone answering machine keep track of Wendy's progress. They are snatches of the most intense, powerful, emotional, exhausting ten weeks of our lives. They highlight the positive, but the journal entries tell of how things really are for me. We are positive people. We consciously choose the positive. We do not entertain the negative. We totally disallow it. We record the messages we leave and of the people who call. Our first message is not recorded. There were three messages left for us.

Phone Message: Dec. 9. Wed.

Hi!, this is your morning report! More good news. Wendy has had her intra-cranial probe removed. Now treatment is total rest for her dear brain, so visitors are cancelled for about five days.

There are 18 messages.

People are catching on. We are overwhelmed by the number of people who respond, who send flowers to us and to her, who write precious notes to us and who send us cards and letters saying that they are devastated by what has happened.

Journal Entry: December 9, 1987

How many tears are there?

Phone Message: Fri. Dec. 12.
Doctors are pleased with Wendy's progress. The coma seems to
be lightening. They are going to try to take her off the
respirator again today. Keep those prayers and positive
thoughts directed her way. She's listening. Thank you for your
messages. They really help our exhaustion.

There are 20 messages.

The messages tell us of the prayers which are being said around the world. They tell of friends and family thinking and caring about us. They tell us that someone is bringing supper the following evening.

I phone Batya Chivers, the clinical social worker, who I began seeing after my successful back surgery in August. I want to be sure that I stay well. I want to know if there is a psychological component to my back problems so that I will remain healthy. I have an appointment scheduled. I phone her to tell her I can't come. "My daughter is in a coma in the hospital," I say. She replies, "Mufty, will anything bad happen to Wendy if you don't come to this appointment?" I say, "No, I just feel I should be there." "Come to me," she said insistently, "it is really important that you come to me" and so I go.

Journal Entry: December 12th 1987

I tried to tell Batya what had happened but I cried and cried. She is so grounded. She just held me, rocking me, supporting me as I told her of Wendy's terrible accident, about Wendy in a coma and how I couldn't bear it. My heart broke. She encouraged me to cry, to sob, to keen, to rage, to rant, to experience in every bone this terrible reality. It felt so natural to be held in the warm arms of another woman, a woman who has also given birth, nursed, nurtured and named a child.

Creatively, Bruce decides that Wendy is missing all these visitors who come to the hospital. He makes a great cardboard sheet, puts it up on the wall and invites people to bring photographs of themselves so we can create a grand collage of her friends.

Phone Message: Sun., Dec. 14.

Wendy was moved out of intensive care today to ward 4A2. She can have visitors now but she is still in a coma. Bring a photo of yourself so that we can stick it on a great collage and Wendy will know who visited while she was in her coma.

There are 9 messages.

Journal Entry: December 15, 1987

The sun shines, but I have wept the morning away. Tom is moving his and Wendy's things out of their house. He brought over boxes of Wendy's belongings, her books, clothes, pictures and with Doug's help, has put them up over the garage. But, he says, the stuff she will want as soon as she wakes up, her makeup and her purse, he put in a suitcase on a bed in our spare room. Her purse was so difficult for me to see. She is so much a part of me that our purses are almost the same. We both carry similar date books, the same kind of lipstick, hand lotion and always have too many pencils and pens in our purses. How can I lose my daughter?

Phone Message: Tues., Dec. 16, 1987

Wendy is holding her own. She is having her tracheotomy tube blocked at intervals so that she can breath and cough out her mouth. She is still in a coma which is obviously a safe place for her to be. Visitors are encouraged to talk and laugh with her. Thanks for your messages!

There are 3 messages.

Journal Entry: December 17, 1987
I am trying to think how to write a Christmas letter because slowly it dawns on me that it is not fair to the others just to concentrate on Wendy. Bob and his fiancé, Shelley have a wedding in the year ahead, and Kory, our new grandson, needs to be announced.

I hear that Lydia Kehoe and some other friends created a box of strong scents so that when they go to visit Wendy they put her through an aroma therapy session. They have lemon, wintergreen, cinnamon, cloves, peppermint, banana, chili, and sweet-smelling perfumes of all sorts. They even have disagreeable, offensive smells like ammonia and gasoline. Wendy's face registers displeasure with the ammonia. She responds!

I realize that Christmas holidays are coming soon and hospital staffing is at a bare minimum during those times. I ask Wendy's physiotherapist to show us what passive movements we might do with Wendy so that she won't miss any during the holidays. She says yes, she can teach a few people. Thirteen friends turn up for the lesson. I take pictures in the dark and crowded room.

Phone Message: Thurs., Dec 18.
We are all most encouraged. Wendy seems to be looking at people and is more responsive. The family had a great physio lesson today and Wendy was sat on the side of the bed. Then Tom and Bruce and Mairead and Lydia got her into a wheelchair and out to the sitting room area....Yea Team!

There are 4 messages.

Someone gives us a book about miracles. In it there is a Miracle Action Plan. I copy it out to have it near. It says "Know what you want your miracle to be. Visualize it happening!"

Phone Message: Sat., Dec. 20.

Wendy has had an active day. She is still unconscious but lighter. A big miracle occurred today. Her right leg has been moving through full range, toes and all. Now we have to work on her right arm.. Visitors welcome. Don't bring things as there is no room. Thanks for your messages and prayers.

There are 4 messages.

Journal Entry: December 20, 1988.

A desolate day yesterday. I sat for an hour and a half, alone with Wendy who was sitting up in a wheel chair out in the atrium. She was flailing about and I was terrified. She is so strong and I, so weak. I felt abandoned. My back hurt. I was really angry that life isn't fair!. I finally realized I had to look after myself, so I took Wendy back into her room and went to the ladies' room for a pee before driving home. I sat on a seat, wet with someone else's urine. I was livid. It tipped the balance of my sanity. I drove home, screaming in the car. In the garage I just sat in the car and grunted and groaned, giving birth to the pain and anger, getting it out of my body. I hit the horn in my fury and Bill came out to find me in this dreadful distress. He wept trying to hold me, trying to help me, thinking I had seen something terrible which he didn't yet know.

We lay on our bed weeping.

Later I asked a friend to come help me walk in the quiet ravine. There we met a former student of mine with her husband, running up the path. The last time I had talked with her, he was in a coma from a bicycle accident. Today he was running up our ravine. It was the miracle I needed at that moment to help me look ahead.

Journal Entry: December 21, 1987

I understand anguish. Today Bill and I went up to the hospital. We wheeled Wendy in her chair out to the sun room. Bill's adoration of his daughter, his look, searching her dull eyes for connection, now that she is upright is a picture I will carry in my heart always. Her eyes are open but there is no recognition.

In the atrium there is space and sunlight and airiness. It is a place for lots of friends. Ten of us today. Later Tom said, "I think she wants to sit up," so he sat her on the side of the bed. Her toes touched the floor and without any warning, Wendy stood up. Tom stood with her, and then she sat down. This happened three times!

I am so grateful there are so many people helping. It is amazing to us the numbers of friends who want to be involved. I photographed everyone visiting Wendy today.

Journal Entry: Mon., Dec. 22.

Thoughts return to Wendy, who went down to physiotherapy yesterday with Tom and Lydia. She does an "extensor thrust" which means that when her toes hit the ground, she stiffens in a reflex motion causing her to stand straight up. All are thrilled, except me because I keep hearing "AREAS OF DAMAGE, MEMORY, SPEECH AND COMPREHENSION." What will this mean?

I think to myself, to create a miracle we must visualize what the miracle would be. Exactly what the miracle will be.

Journal Entry: December 23, 1987.

Went to see Wendy this morning. Her right shoulder is losing some spasm. She had another CAT scan to see why she is so nearly conscious but not conscious. The physiotherapist continues to be wonderful; gauging Wendy's tolerance for exercise, pushing her just the right amount. So is Tom. He takes his cue from Wendy, watching her, watching her all the time. I think his ability to watch animals in the wild has equipped him for this vigil.

I went Christmas shopping and bought a teddy bear for Wendy and one for Doug too, because I'd like him to have his own little soft dog. I bought an outfit for Michele, underwear for Bill, and a highchair for Kyle and Kory. It will be a strange Christmas.

Phone Message: Wed., Dec. 24.

Aunty Anne, Bill's sister, and I just came home from being with Wendy this morning. We wheeled her about in a chair. She is still in a coma but we believe she has milliseconds of awareness. She is doing what she needs for healing, so keep those prayers and messages coming. They help us all. Don't forget to hang up your stocking.

There are 4 messages.
We don't hang up stockings this year. A first.

Phone Message: Thurs., Dec. 25.

Merry Christmas. Wendy gave us a gift by moving her right arm at the elbow today. She is still in a coma but improving daily. We hope Santa has been as good to you as he was to us.

There are 8 messages .

Journal Entry: December 25, 1987

Bill went to see Bruce and Michele last night. Then he cried all the way home. He went into the back bedroom, cried and prayed on his knees.

When we got up to the hospital last night, we found a card from the Kehoes with the promise of an Erin Irish Knit sweater, hand knit by Ann, at a later date, with a beautiful letter saying how much they loved her. Wendy was extra special to them too. This Christmas, no grapefruit, no oranges, no stockings, no Wendy.

Bill and I woke early and we snuggled, needing strength from one another on this strange Christmas Day. I couldn't handle a morning visit to Wendy, so he went off alone with a big, fuzzy white bear for Tom that he will leave with Wendy.

Journal Entry: December 27, 1987

Aunty Anne and I both saw Wendy's mouth moving yesterday, in response to something I asked her. Then Tom said she smiled with half her face!

A soft diet was ordered, but she has no mouth control. She has trouble with the gag reflex, and tongue control. When the orderly was tubbing her and then dressing her, he said "Put the bad arm in first", as he pulled her right arm through her T-shirt. I wanted to shout, "Wendy doesn't have a bad arm!"

Phone Message: Sun., Dec. 28.

Wendy smiled today and even had a tear in her eye shortly thereafter. Still in a light coma, she sits up and stands up for a minute or so. Direct your prayers to her right arm and swallowing. Mathewsons recover best when eating solid food!

There are 5 messages.

Journal Entry: December 28, 1987

A night nurse uses the expression, "Locked In". Wendy knows some things such as how to put her arm through her T-shirt but she is just not quite connecting with us. Diane says Wendy needs to be away where she is safe. Wendy will stay there as long as she needs to. I am lonely without her.

Journal Entry: December 29, 1987

Wendy stares at us, unseeing. It is as though she is distraught, unable to know anything. She constantly moves her legs, trying to climb out of bed. She is in a canvas restraint belt. She feels her stubble-like hair and red, S-shaped scar. She rubs her nose. She rubs her left eye, all with her left hand. The right arm lies by her side, useless, but the spasm is subsiding. Her mouth has crusty lips. She is unable to swallow or to gag.

When Tom visits, he takes off her restraint. He allows her to move about as she needs. She repeatedly climbs sideways in the bed, pushing at the bars with her feet. When Tom sits her on the side of the bed and her feet touch the floor, she stands and walks a few steps. Then she sits down again and climbs back into bed. Her eyes close. Almost immediately, they open again. She tries again. And again. And again. It is exhausting being with her, trying to interpret her needs. I take pictures of Wendy and Tom, of the restraints, of Wendy's open eyes, of the nurses working with her, of Bill talking to her.

Wendy pulled her stomach tube out last night. This is how she is being fed. She is very thin now. She needs operating room time to replace it today.

I arranged for me and Tom to see Wendy's x-rays and CAT scans. Tom was in the hospital when Bill and I saw them first. I had to be quite insistent to get them. I also requested that Wendy be moved to a bed on the courtyard side of the ward so she can be in real daylight from the atrium. The cold and snow have come at last. I have only enough energy for sorrow.

Practical, strong and capable Shelley drives Bob from Lethbridge in southern Alberta to Edmonton, laid out in the back of their truck. He has just had back surgery to remove a disc. They want to be close to Edmonton to visit Wendy. They stay with us.

Journal Entry: December 31, 1987

Bob was knocked out with the reality of Wendy's struggle. He told me that he cried a lot for her last night. "She looks to me," he said, "like a prisoner from the war camps, hair shaved, vacuous look, thin...." We agree that she has a haunted look.

Bruce took Wendy into the quiet room yesterday morning and phoned Bill. He gave the phone to Wendy who tried to speak but instead cried. Bruce cried also. Bruce has a week off work and is spending his mornings with Wendy. I flood with gratitude that Wendy's brothers are so attentive and care so much.

We have no plans for this evening and will probably be in bed asleep when the new year comes. We must ask for strength.

Phone Message: Thurs., Jan. 1, 1988

Happy New Year to all. Bob and Shelley, and Doug are here. Bruce and Michele, Kyle and Kory are coming over for spiced beef between one and three. Wendy saw the New Year in still in her coma. She is still restless and needs to be restrained all the time. She is beginning to make sounds in her throat. Visualize a strong right arm for her and lots of swallowing and talking with us. It is good to look forward to Wendy's own Olympics in 1988.

There are 5 messages.

A routine develops for visiting Wendy. Bruce goes very early in the morning. He has organized a Walkman for her pillow and keeps her own tapes up to date so she can have her favourite music. He laughs with Wendy. Mairead, lovely, tall, fun-loving Mairead, with her curly, bouncing, brown hair often drops in on her way to work. She helps with Wendy's shower, getting in with her , laughing and giggling, like girl friends do. I arrive about nine and bring news of who has phoned. Tom goes about eleven each day. He is getting stronger. He wears his cowboy hat. It seems to get a response from Wendy. He swears she can see it and recognize it. He stays until about five. Then many odds and sods come in the evening. It is wonderful that we are all available. Bob, Shelley, Tom, Bill and Doug are all off work and I am on disability leave because of my recent back surgery.

Phone Message: Mon., Jan 4.

We don't know for sure but we think Wendy is coming around. She is smiling when people like Tom, Mufty and Bill say Hello. Tom and Bruce are making miracles by not knowing hospital policy, walking her up and down the stairs. Things are looking good so keep the messages coming. Thank you.

Phone Message: Later that same day.

Tom is ecstatic because Wendy really smiled at him. She walked down to therapy and made all the physios ecstatic too. Tom called her a little shit disturber and she smiled at him. So Wendy made Tom happy. He told his parents, making them happy, his parents phoned and made us happy and now we're telling you, making you happy.

There are 6 messages.

Journal Entry: January 4, 1988

Yesterday, Bruce tells us, Tom walked Wendy up and down four flights of stairs three times. I gasped, heart-shocked that he would do so much, yet I know he only follows her lead. Bill, shocked too, said this is too much. She is going to have a relapse. A giant relapse. But that's not true.

Slowly the realization dawns on me. The miracle is happening! The miracle is that Bruce, Tom, Bob and Mairead and Lydia are there beside her, unlocking her, letting her do what she can.

On Saturday the 3rd, Tom took her into the bathroom, took off her diapers, which she was trying to do, and she had a bowel movement in the toilet. A giant step. Yesterday she had a pee in the bathroom. Somewhere behind that strained unresponsive face is Wendy who knows how to care for her body, and is trying. And the miracle is that there are the "troops" at her side ready to help her. Jubilation from all who know her.

Bill and I went out for dinner and managed to enjoy ourselves considerably. We drove to the hospital on our way home at 9.30. Wendy was sleeping peacefully with her right hand resting, fingers relaxed over her tummy. No spasm evident. We kissed her gently and tip-toed away.

Journal Entry: January 7, 1988

I took Wendy to Occupational Therapy, (OT) and to Speech Therapy today and then I looked her right in the face and said slowly and clearly, "Wen, would you like some ice cream?" Three little nods of the head. So we waited in line, she in her wheelchair, me pushing. I bought a dish of creamy vanilla, found a table and fed Wendy a tiny first bite. She swallowed it! Another bite, she opened wider. She swallowed it. Another spoonful. She swallowed. So precisely, so obediently, like a dear child of one. My daughter is eating again! Satisfaction, just like feeding the babies.

We talked to Tom about giving him some funds so that he would not feel *so anxious about going back to work. He accepted it saying, "She gave up a $40,000 a year job to come with me for the summer. I feel it is my job now to give her at least three months." His love is another miracle!*

Journal Entry: January 9, 1988

I went to the first day of an Acupuncture seminar with Dr. Steven Aung yesterday. He told me about the area of speech for acupuncture and suggested I rub a particular point of Wendy's wrist in a counter clockwise movement for fifteen minutes. I was exhausted from concentrating at the seminar, but went to see Wendy on my way home. Mairead was there with two others. They talked with Wen while I rubbed the spot. Wendy found it unpleasant and tried to pull her arm away. One of the lads went off to buy her some chocolate. I said good night and went home. Mairead phoned me and said, "When the fellow came back in the room, Wendy said to him, "How are you? How are you?" It took me ages until I realized that Wendy had spoken her first words! Spoken them right after I had done the acupressure on the spot Dr. Aung suggested. How thrilling! More miracle that I had registered for the course before the accident!

Phone Message: Mon. Jan 11.

It was decided that Wendy was to have a plate put in her head. Bill spent four hours waiting to speak to the doctor to be convinced that this was really necessary.

There are 3 messages.

Journal Entry: January 11, 1988

I need to write. Wendy goes back to surgery this morning to have an acrylic plate put in her skull. The tension is high. Bill is devastated by this news. He sobbed and sobbed into his pillow saying again and

again, "But she is so vulnerable, my little girl. She is just a little,
weenie girl" and it is true. She is so trusting at this point, looking
around, checking for approval. Vulnerable and trusting.

> ### Phone Message: Tues., Jan 12.
> *Wendy had surgery today. It went well. She is back on the ward*
> *needing watching as she wants to pull off her bandages. She*
> *also needs help feeding at meal times. If you want to help with*
> *5pm or 7pm or 9pm times, please leave your number.*

There are 3 messages.

Journal Entry: January 12, 1988

I want to record that we began to feed Wendy on Saturday the ninth.
Bill went with her to OT and Speech yesterday. He watched her try the
puzzles and tasks. He saw her lack of comprehension. That was part of
his pain yesterday. A greater awareness of some more of her injury.
I told Wendy that our dear, long-time, next door neighbour died
yesterday. First, Wendy had a slow worried frown, then a huge look of
trying to understand and then a look almost of horror, real sadness and
then tears with small, guttural throat sounds. Poor darling.
She looks so vulnerable, but it is her saving grace. She doesn't drool or
have fits or spasms or other disquieting or difficult traits which would
make people want to avoid her. She smiles and laughs which makes
people want to be with her. The more people who are with her, who
become involved in her recovery, who stimulate her, talk to her, laugh
with her, the better her opportunity for full recovery. This too, is part
of the miracle.

Unbeknownst to us, Tom takes Wendy's black dog, Bear, up to
the hospital, parks in the underground parking lot which is connected
by elevator to her floor. Then he goes upstairs, gets Wendy in a

wheelchair and takes her down to meet Bear. Bear climbs up on her lap and licks her face. Wendy feels her, pats her, and laughs that Tom has brought her. They leave Bear in the truck and Tom takes Wendy back to the ward and says nothing.

Journal Entry: January 13, 1988.

I went early this morning to be with Wendy. She had pulled the heavy, large, white bandage off in the night and pulled out her drain from the scar in her head. She was very thirsty and drank three glasses of water shortly after I arrived. She threw up. After she went to the bathroom, she threw up again. She kept trying to take her bandage off so it was a full time occupation just to keep her hands from creeping up, tugging and pulling.

About nine, tiring, I asked the nurse to watch her while I phoned Bill to come and help. When I got back, the bandage was off. I could see her half shaven head, swollen on the surgery side. We put the bandage back on and just kept watch. She looked brighter after a while and sat in the chair while the nurse made her bed.

When we got her back to bed we gave her more water and apple juice in small amounts. Then milk. I took some more pictures. Sometime after the apple juice, she began to talk. "That's nice." "That's nice," she said and then she babbled on and on and on in total gibberish in the dear voice that has been so long silent. Oh what treasured sound! To hear her speak after so many weeks. Her sweet voice was so lovely, so gentle, so precious to me. And so.... let me visualize her speaking, clearly and concisely and comprehending what is said to her.

Phone Message: Thurs., Jan. 14.

Wendy continues to improve from her Tuesday surgery. You have all been terrific. She is on the same ward but in a different room. Thanks for your prayers.

There are 6 messages.

Journal Entry: January 15, 1988

Yesterday Wendy went to x-ray in a wheelchair for a swallowing test. Great results! Her tongue and mouth are working as they should. Imagine, two days after having surgery to replace her skull bone with a plastic part she is up and around, having swallowing x-rays. I took pictures of Wendy and Tom at x-ray and also of the x-ray pictures of the swallowing. Her half-shaved head is hard for me to see again.

Last night I went to Camera Club. Only two people there had heard of Wendy's accident. It was strange, as it has been the total focus of our lives for over six weeks. I was glad I went. It was refreshing to think about something else.

Doug just phoned to tell me that last night he went up and May Hentschel, Wendy's strong, skiing and hiking friend, was there from Jasper. Wendy was trying to tell her what had happened. He said you could understand what she was trying to say!

She is pointing to the people on the big collage of pictures that Bruce organized. It is a great tool for Wendy to use when she can't tell us names. More of the miracle!

Bruce did his electronic wizardry and created a tape recorder and played back what she said. She was frustrated but it was wonderful to know that she understood.

Bill and I need to get away for a weekend. I phoned people to ask them for two hour commitments while we are gone. Everyone seemed delighted to be asked so Wendy will have people to feed her and be with her while we are away.

Phone Message: Fri., Jan 15.

Wendy is so great that Bill and I are taking off for the weekend. Doug will be around and there are lots of helpers for Wendy's feeding at meal time. Thank you all for everything. If you want a more personal message, call Bruce or Michele.

There are 5 messages.

Journal Entry: January 16, 1988. Red Deer Lodge.

We made it to Red Deer.......exhausted! Wept on the way with relief that Wendy is alive. Before I left I bought three yellow roses and some cheesecake for Wendy. When I gave Wendy the flowers she slowly connected that they were for her. She was happy to know that she was understood and that things are hard for her. Tom, Wendy and I cried. Tom went off for his lunch break and Wendy ate and loved the cheesecake. I had brought some of her own clothes. She put them on immediately and then we sat comfortably together. Mother and daughter. Our daughter is coming back!

Phone Message: Mon., Jan. 18.

Wendy is doing better every day. She went home with Tom on Saturday and he took her out for a walk around the hospital yesterday. She has a half Iroquois hairdo, since her Tuesday surgery and 26 clamps in the S-shaped scar over her ear. She is bright eyed and eating!

There are 2 messages.

The days are busy. Bill is job searching. He goes to Calgary for an interview. I have the house to myself to work on some house work. It feels good but the many phone interruptions make me cross. Then when it is Bruce, who is doing so much for Wendy, and I am cranky, I feel awful.

There are lots of people in our house. Bob and Shelley have moved to Edmonton and are staying with us while they house hunt.

They have their friends in. They are very considerate but they are there. Wendy has tons of visitors now. Yesterday there were visitors from Peace River. It was like a zoo last night with seven of us there. I get upset watching the circus around her and all the noise, so I leave. The numbers don't seem to bother Wendy.

Phone Message: Thurs., Jan. 21.
This is Bob, who saw Wendy last night for the first time in a week. The progress is incredible and hard to explain fully through a machine. She is beginning to communicate her needs through pointing and facial expressions and is trying very hard to develop some speech. She is beginning to count and also to draw and write. Her scar seems to be healing well and it seems she will be moving to the Glenrose Hospital soon. Please keep your love, prayers and messages coming.

There are 3 calls.

I go to a day-long seminar on brain injury, for professionals only. I go under the guise of physiotherapist, but in my mind I am there as a mother. I remember none of the day's presentation, but I clearly remember a question asked at the end of the day.

"What do you say to the family when you know the outcome is very bad and they think their loved one will go back to college? How do you tell the family not to expect too much?"

He answered. "Never underestimate a family. Let me tell you a story. When I was an intern, there was a young man of 19 just coming out of a coma. His brain injury was extensive. The family thought he would return to college, and the medical experts thought he would never leave an institution."

"Eight years later when I was in a different city at a teaching hospital, I met the same young man in the hall. He was in a wheelchair and was on his way to a class. He was taking one course at college. The family was right. He had returned to college with the help of his strong family who had hired tutors and therapists of many kinds over the years."

"It is a matter of perspective. Like the drawing you learned in art class, of railway tracks meeting in the distance, each side begins far apart and as time passes, the medical people learn and the families learn, and the two lines converge and the two points of view meet in the distance." "I now know," he said, "never to underestimate the power of a family."

Journal Entry: January 21, 1988.

I miss you so much, Wendy, I need to write you a letter in this journal so I'm the only one who knows how I miss you. Maybe it will bring you closer.

Dear Wendy,

Yesterday I wanted to talk to you so badly about everything that has happened in the past two months but you're not here yet. I need you to know how much I miss you.

Yesterday you had your stomach tube taken out. Mairead, Tom and Dad spent the morning with you and Doug much of the afternoon. Bob and Shelley are moving to Edmonton because they want to be near so they can help.

I went shopping and banking by myself but I wanted you to be with me. I wanted us to have coffee together so we could chat. I wanted to have a gab-fest with you, the way we used to. I value your point of view. Just you and me. Where are you, Wendy?

You, my precious daughter, are sitting, cross-legged on your bed, happily greeting the myriad of people who find their way to your bedside. You seem so vulnerable somehow. Unable to say, "Go home." or "Leave me alone" or "Stop making me play your word games." My heart is torn wanting to protect you, wanting to know what you need without your being able to tell us. The other evening seemed like such an ongoing circus in your room that both your father and I had to leave to get away from what we felt was too much. And yet you seemed fine. I think you can only focus on one person at a time, or maybe two.

Now I feel better having written to you. I think you have answered that you are OK. Thank you for being the person you are, for cheerfully greeting all your visitors, for trying so hard in all the word tasks given to you by Bruce, Tom, Doug and Mairead. They are all doing a great job. I miss you.. but you are coming back. I love you, darling. Mum.

Journal Entry: January 21. 11pm
Wendy told Bob and his friend to go home tonight by pointing to their jackets. Hurray! She can protect herself!

Phone Message: Sat., Jan 23.
Wendy is out for the weekend! She is with Tom in St. Albert at 459-7440. We went out to visit this morning and did the dishes together. Wendy dried and put away! Wowie! Bob and Shelley have an apartment and are moving to Edmonton. We are going to the opera.

There are 3 messages.

Phone Message: Tues., Jan 26.
Wendy is at Tom's house for the duration of the nurses' strike. They can be reached at 459-7440.

No messages!

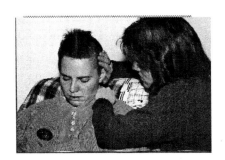

Chapter 7

The Nurses' Strike

An insert here about my back problems. Oh, tedious, boring, tiresome subject! I include it here because difficulties with my spine have shaped much of my life and my abilities as a mother. I rarely see myself as disabled, but many problems with my back, three spinal operations, the necessity to rest, my inability to sit comfortably for more that twenty minutes at a time, my resulting difficulty travelling by car, the necessity to wear runners with shock-absorbing soles, have all greatly affected my life and thus my childrens' lives.

I managed through those years of pain and inability with the help and support of Bill. He never blamed me, never complained about all I've been unable to do, and willingly assumed many of the traditional mother roles without complaint. At the swimming pool, Bill took the children to the changing room, all four of them, as I was unable to bend to pull on their bathing suits, or take them to a washroom in a public place. I often felt intensely inadequate as a mother.

My first operation, a spinal fusion, was in 1963 with very poor results and more than a year of convalescence. In 1975, another spinal fusion above the last produced excellent results. I then had ten pretty good years. In 1987 tests showed that because of former fusions, the bones above the fusions were growing into the spinal cord, causing weakness and paralysis in my leg muscles. This meant another operation where the bones were chiselled away from the inside of the bony archway that shelters the spinal cord. I had decompression surgery to remove that bone just a few months before Wendy's accident. The results were immediate. The pain decreased and the muscles began to strengthen.

I went regularly to physiotherapy, rebuilding the muscle power in my legs and back. I was having counselling to determine if there was a psychological factor to my back pain. It was good that I had begun the counselling before the accident. Batya, my counsellor, taught me how to care for myself while I was caring for Wendy. She taught me to honour my weak back, to stop feeling guilty for all the things I had been unable to do for my children, and to learn how better to live with myself. I meditate each morning to ground myself. I work at my exercises daily and walk regularly. I was still recuperating from my operation when Wendy's accident took place.

On Tuesday, January 26th, Wendy is discharged from the University Hospital into Tom's care because of a nurses' strike. Tom says they will live at his parents' house in St. Albert. Jim and Ann are away for the winter. During this time we visit them and see that Tom and Wendy are happy to be together again.

Journal Entry: January 31, 1988

Wendy took out the chess men and placed them on the right places on the board, says Tom's brother, Dan. Then yesterday, Doug phoned Tom in St. Albert to tell him he was coming out to visit. Wendy answered the phone. She said. "Hi". "Yes". "Sorry". "Thanks a lot". "Bye". This is her total vocabulary now. Then she hung up.

When Doug arrived he found Wendy writing on a note the word

DOUG, trying to tell Tom that Doug was coming. What hopeful signs!

Wendy phones me as often as she feels like it, using whatever words she has. It is good to have her initiating all this activity.

One evening, Tom takes Wendy swimming. Bill and I meet them at the pool. I have my camera to take pictures. Tom asks Wendy to dive off the side of the pool. I wince, thinking that he should just ask her to climb down the ladder for the first time, but I keep my mouth shut and adjust my flash. She dives in well. I shoot. She comes up smiling. I shoot. Tom and Bill are in the pool and get her to do the butterfly. I watch, carefully, because I think she will go crookedly down the pool because of her weaker right arm. Not at all. She swims as straight as ever before. I make another shot. Then Tom demonstrates a racing turn. I think, "No, Tom, not a racing turn, so soon!" but she comes to the end of the pool, dives under, bends up her knees, turns, flips and pushes herself off hard from the wall of the pool, all underwater.

She surfaces with a heavenly smile on her face which tells us all how good it feels for her to be in her own familiar medium, the water. I click, advance, click and wind, click and wind, grateful that Wendy is not afraid of choking or swallowing water after being on a trach tube for so long.

Later, when she comes to our house, she pulls a card from a Winnipeg friend out of her pocket. When I ask, "Do you want to phone him, Wendy?" She nods yes. What a thrill that she can initiate an idea and creatively communicate it to us.

Our home is still a central meeting place for everyone. All the friends are delighted that Wendy is out and about. They come to visit. Intellectually I know it is wonderful to have this huge number of people around to help, but I am feeling invaded. Bill is out of work, so he is home now. Bob and Shelley live with us while house hunting.

They have their friends too. Wendy and Tom and their friends drop in often, interrupting whatever we are doing, needing coffee, needing an update and words of enthusiasm. Friends are excited and want to see Wendy and hear about her personal victories. There seem to be people around day and night. Too many, too much, too often.

I am quietly going crazy. I need some quiet time. Some space for myself, some time to rest, to heal, to gather myself together, to get the house in order after these months of disorder and confusion. I am not used to letting people know what I want or what I need. But my work with Batya tells me that I must. Even when it is Wendy who needs so much, I must learn to ask for what I need, so that I can be strong for her and her recovery.

I want to ask our children to please phone before they drop in. It seems there is never a moment to be still, to think, to gather my thoughts and be quiet. Bill thinks this is excessive, that we will stop the flow of people who just want to drop in on the spur of the moment because they are in the neighbourhood. He thinks I am being unreasonable. I tell him maybe I am, maybe I'm not, but I need some solitude. People will still care and want to come, but I need a little time and space to myself. All I am asking is that our children phone before they come. I try to tell Bill what is happening to me and how hard it is for me. He says he will support my decision.

Bill and I call a family conference, like we used to do when the children were little and we had a problem. I formulate what I want to say to them and we invite them all on a Sunday afternoon. I feel selfish at having to ask this of them and cry a bit, but Bill is warming to the idea, since he offered his support. I ask them all, Bruce and Michele, Bob and Shelley, Doug, and even Wendy and Tom to let me know before they come. I tell them I feel vulnerable, that I am always at their beck and call, and that I am worn out.

They are surprised at this request. Some are fine with it; others are affronted, and see this as unreasonable. We talk and finally they all agree to my request. They do not necessarily understand, but for a while they agree to my request. I feel good about being able to ask.

The summer before her accident, Wendy had bought tickets to several of the February Winter Olympic events in Calgary. She was planning her next Uneek Experience. We say to Tom, "What are you going to do with the tickets?" He says, "We're going to go and use them!"

So they go to the Calgary Olympics, staying in a borrowed apartment. Tom takes Wendy to all the events they have tickets for. They see alpine skiing, rodeo, hockey, and bobsled events. Wendy falls asleep several times a day. She naps, snoozes, dozes her way through the events. If she gets really tired Tom takes her to the apartment.

Chapter 8

The Glenrose Hospital

On February 15th the nurses' strike is over and Wendy is admitted to the Glenrose Rehabilitation Hospital in Edmonton to begin the rehabilitation phase of her recovery. She is assessed in every department and we are included in many interviews. I go to most of the departments and photograph Wendy with her many new therapists.

Journal Entry: February 27, 1988
I cried a lot today after my interview with Social Services at the Glenrose. It is so hard to read the literature about brain damage and to have labels applied to our Wendy.

Wendy's weekly schedule includes all disciplines at the Glenrose. In physiotherapy she progresses quickly with balance, co-ordination, and strengthening exercises. In occupational therapy she works with communication and daily living skills. Speech therapy is the most intensive, with attention to comprehension and speaking. Words. Words. Words. She tries to read. She is given tapes of the material she is trying to read so she will hear what the words sound like while she reads the script. She goes to psychology once a week, but has little insight into her problems. Her recreation therapy is managed by a colleague of hers who says Wendy keeps ahead of him in organizing all her social activities. It is true. Visitors come to the hospital to see Wendy but she has arranged to be doing something away from the hospital every minute she can. She goes out in the evenings and on weekends, or when nothing else is scheduled.

Journal Entry: Saturday, March 8, 1988 4:25 am
Wendy took me into the bathroom and pointed to her uterus. "Are you menstruating?" I ask. Her head nods. I showed her where things are. My heart soaring with joy. One more step on the return to normal. Another miracle.

Wendy becomes insistent that we understand her. She no longer accepts "some day" but now speaks louder and stays focused longer. She is enormously creative in her communications. She calls Tom "That guy I love" and me, "That girl, my favourite."

A neighbour gives Wendy a session with a woman healer who is, they say, a channel for Han Wan, an ancient Chinese Healer from the fourth century. It can't hurt! Wendy has a long session which I attend. It is extraordinary to watch this woman change into an elderly man. She rubs Wendy's arms and legs and tells us to ask him/her questions. Wendy does and gets vague, promising answers. It feels very strange to be there but we feel that if there is the slightest chance that this visit will help Wendy, and won't hurt her, we try it and are grateful to our neighbours. I photograph the session for my slide show.

There is a team meeting at the Glenrose to discuss the assessments of each rehab team member and to plan further rehabilitation. I am upset. I feel vulnerable and weepy that people are evaluating Wendy. I tape it. Wendy attends with Tom, Bruce, Bob, Bill and myself. We hear from nursing, occupational therapy, recreation therapy, physiotherapy, speech therapy, psychology and social services.

Journal Entry: March 24, 1988

Last night, Bill wept and wept and wept after our meeting with the head of the Brain Injury Unit at the Glenrose. This really nice doctor was quite clear that Wendy will have months and months of speech therapy and psychology, probably years. Since that meeting, Bill has been devastated.

She also said that Wendy is rare in types of head injuries in that she is a university graduate. Often, patients have a maximum grade nine education and no work experience. The fact that Wendy is so motivated to learn is very much in her favour.

Wendy has a weekend pass, so she and Tom borrow a country house from our dear friends, Franny and Bill Hall. Wendy writes a thank-you letter for the loan. She draws two childlike figures in bathing suits with disconnected feet on the female. She writes:

Dear F   Wendy and Tom   Olympics
Alpine Skiing   Hockey   Rodeo   Big Tone   Bobsled

There is an unselfconsciousness in Wendy, sending these infantile attempts. I am torn between being encouraged that she does it and devastated at comparing this note to the work of our university graduate.

Journal Entry: April 6, 1988

I bought my van yesterday! Called it Vanessa. I can stand up straight in it, cook, keep things cold, use an indoor port-a-potty and a firm bed. I have wanted one for so long and finally, triggered by my new awareness that anything can happen in a second of time, decided to buy one. I can get away in it so I can do photography and stop any time to rest on a bed I know will be hard enough.

It is my escape van to go away from the city to see the vast skies of Alberta, to taste the fresh wind of the prairies, to watch stars away from the thief of city lights. In it I will seek mountains reflected in lakes, camp beside streams and smell the harvest.

I plan a trip in "Vanessa Van", to the interior of B.C. The trip is a get-away time for me. I have been trying to work on "Health and Healing," the slide show I am scheduled to present in July in Regina, Saskatchewan. But finding any time for this work is impossible. Bruce visits without phoning, dropping in, leaving Michele and kids in the car. I feel terrible while they sit outside. I tell him again, "I am still recuperating from major surgery. Please, think about me. I need my rest. I have a disability." I love him but I must be allowed to plan my time.

We have a niece visiting from Montreal. Tom comes in unexpectedly from Rocky Mountain House, Alberta where he is working. The house is still like Grand Central Station, where I am expected to be delighted to see everyone come in the door. I am not. I have work to do. It is too much.

Bill and I are growing apart. We are both preoccupied with how we can make Wendy better. We have lost the intimacy of our marriage. We live like brother and sister. Convenient, practical, yet there is no real exchange between us. I run away to think about all these things.

Journal Entry: April 28, 1988.

Happy Birthday to me! I am out in beautiful Finn Creek, in the mountains, just west of Field, British Columbia. I celebrated by walking 2.4 kilometres to Wapta Falls from the end of the road. The

quiet and the solitude are blissful and I am thrilled that my legs are
strong enough to climb down the side of the waterfall.

It has been five months since Wendy's accident. She is
discharged from the Glenrose Hospital. She will have outpatient
treatments from now on.

There is nowhere for Wendy to go. I am away in my van and
Tom is working in Rocky Mountain House. It is decided that she will
fly to Nelson, British Columbia, to join me in the mountains. Then we
will visit her friend in the Crowsnest Pass, drive north on the
Kananaskis highway in Alberta and visit another friend in Calgary.

The day of her flight dawns, or rather doesn't dawn, as it is
teeming rain, dark and totally socked in at the airport. I think her plane
will be diverted to Cranbrook, B.C. How will Wendy cope alone with
her limited speech? How will I find her?

I phone Bill. He rushes out to the airport where Tom is seeing
her off and gives her a paper with the phone number of where I can be
found. I am terrified for her, but the weather clears, the Nelson airport
opens up and the plane lands safely. She had charmed her seat mate, a
distinguished-looking, older business man, with her story, in hesitant
limited speech, and enlisted his help. I am incredibly relieved to see her
and she seems happy to see me too. After much hugging with relief, we
drive off to Winlaw, B. C., to see Pam and Sandy, our artist friends who
were with us the night of Wendy's accident.

We have a great visit. Their eight-year old, golden-haired
daughter, Tara, dances a special dance for Wendy, with cartwheels and
handstands, and they both enjoy each other. We stay another day,
meditate with the family, walk in the outdoors, see their art and then we
take our leave.

We drive south through Nelson and then cross choppy, blue
Kootenay Lake on the ferry. I photograph all the way. We stop for lunch

at a newly-opened lodge. While I am in the washroom, Wendy tries to strike up a conversation with the owner, who is making lunch. The woman cannot understand what Wendy is saying. She does not take the time to listen. I can see that the woman is not impressed with this odd-sounding young woman trying to speak to her. She wants to be left alone. Immediately, I realize that she thinks Wendy is retarded. This is a first, one I had not considered. It pierces my heart. During lunch I tell Wendy that I think the woman thinks she is retarded and Wendy says, "Yes, Mum." And I can see that Wendy agrees with me.

The rest of the trip is pleasant. We meet Wendy's friends Lee-Anne and Gary Walker in Fernie, BC. Lee-Anne is also in the recreation business. Wendy rides on the back of Gary's motorcycle all the way to the ranch where we have dinner. I watch out the back of the van, terrified that she will lose her balance. I worry about her falling, getting dizzy, not holding on tight enough, but I decide I must be led by what Wendy thinks she can do. I say nothing. She is fine.

She spends the day at the newly-opened tourist attraction "Head-Smashed-In Buffalo Jump". I write in my journal: "the name alone is so violent for me that I am unable to go."

The next evening two Calgary friends of Wendy's join us at a campground on the Sheep River, south of Calgary. The sun sets behind the mauve mountains, the river meanders eastward gurgling softly beside the trembling aspens and the campfire smells woody. We have dinner around the fire and swap stories. It feels wonderfully normal.

Journal Entry: May 9, 1988
When we got back to Edmonton, I just collapsed, grateful I could share the responsibility of Wendy with Bill. I feel a great strain being with her all day. This morning I didn't really connect with Bill, as Wendy was up and asking for help with phone calls, letters, projects, and appointments.

There is no more hospitalization. Tom is in Rocky Mountain House. I am still on sick leave. It is agreed that Wendy will live with us while Tom is away. I am grateful that I am well enough to cope but more aware now of how difficult it will be. It frightens me. I wonder how hospitals can send people who have had brain injuries out to families who have had no training in what to do.

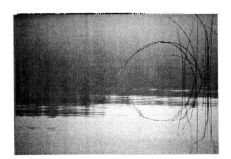

Chapter 9
Summer, 1988

Finally it is summer. Tom has clients to take fishing in northern British Columbia. Wendy stays with us. She has her own sunny, yellow room with her own phone. She is still very thin. Her clothes hang on her bony shoulders. She eats well, when she remembers. Her hair is growing in, a dull brown, not the golden blond as before. The haunted look is gone. Her smile ignites when she sees people. But when she is angry she has a fierce look of fury in her eyes and her mouth tightens. She has lost the social skill of masking her feelings. The fierce look means she is really angry. We read her face all the time, because she still has so few words.

I still go regularly to physiotherapy and to my sessions with Batya. Wendy goes to speech therapy and psychology. My job is now on hold, a personal leave. I plan to return to my physiotherapy job at the Workers Compensation Board on the first of September.

Our days are extremely busy. Wendy wakes very early and stays by herself until she hears us moving about at six. It is hard for her to amuse herself. She does not understand the radio or the T.V and is unable to read. She cannot write either. So she phones people, often long distance. Her ability to reach out to her friends all over Canada is one of her great strengths, so we have told her that we can handle the long distance charges. It is her touchstone to discovering who she is, and who her friends are.

I am working on the slide show. It is important that I captured Wendy's recovery on film. Wendy does not fully grasp what has happened to her. She still cannot understand the spoken word very well. She knows she has difficulty with understanding, speaking, and writing. I think she feels guilty about it, as though she is not trying hard enough.

I tell Wendy that I have photographs of her while she was in a coma. Would she like to see them? She eagerly says "yes." We sit together with the whirr of the projectors in the dark. I project slides of her in Intensive Care, of her bandaged head, of machines which keep her alive, of her face, expressionless in the greenish colour of the fluorescent hospital lights, of nurses working with her tracheotomy, of visitors, of Tom with his cowboy hat, watching Wendy, getting Wendy out of bed, walking with her. I show her speech therapists, physiotherapists, occupational therapists, x-rays of her swallowing, her time in the Glenrose Hospital, more therapists, more rehabilitation, now smiles and expressions on her face. Slide after slide. I watch Wendy carefully while she watches the pictures, ready to turn off the projector, but she is spellbound.

She is crying when the pictures are finished. I hug her. I say, "It's sad, isn't it Wendy". "No", she says, "I..... cry.... as... hard.... for you." I cry too, full of wonder that she is thinking of us, not of herself.

For the first time, she gets a glimmer of understanding of the journey she has been on. She sees how many friends came to help, how Tom was there, day after day, every day until supper time. He undid her restraints and allowed her to thrash in her bed. He protected her from hurting herself. He decided when she wanted to go to the bathroom. He dressed her, he put on her shoes and walked her around the ward. He was strong, able to redirect her when she tried to climb into cupboards or dark corners to sleep. She tried to climb into the shelf under the nurses desk. He gently took her back to her bed where she climbed back in and then got out again so she could explore her environment again. Wendy saw her haunted look, with her shaven head, her "no-word" world, searching to know what she didn't remember. Those were dark days. Wendy has no memory of that time. The slides have given her information we could never tell her. She understands more now.

Journal Entry: May 17, 1988.
My Health and Healing show had it's "World Premiere" last night, a private showing to a selected audience. On the day of the show I had to rent a table and a screen plus take Wendy to her doctor to check sleeping medications and to do her banking.

The show went fairly well with a few technical difficulties. A friend offered to be my technician. Another example of people showing up when I need them most.

Another friend said that the most significant section of the show is the last, the strongest is about Wendy. She pointed out the special significance of a long umbilical cord of kelp in one of the images, tenaciously hanging on to a rock. She says how strongly that ties with the mother/daughter bond. Some friends are so astute!

Journal Entry: May 20, 1988
A day when I am saying, "Oh Universe, why Wendy? Why that fabulous young woman? Why? Why my daughter? Oh pain, watching her, not aware she has any problems. Seeing her naive trust that everyone will love her. Instead they are annoyed by her. Why Wendy? Why Wendy? Why Wendy?

Last week, she got up two mornings in a row and took her bike over to Doug's house where she asked him for drugs! I became aware that she was wanting marijuana after her visit to Dr. Susan Low. Susan was very clear with Wendy that drugs, like alcohol and marijuana, decrease the effectiveness of the anti-seizure medication. She said, "Don't take them, Wendy. You could have a seizure." Wendy looked like she understood and gave me the impression that she agreed. However when we came out of the doctor's office, Wendy said to me, "What did she say?" She does not understand at all! Doug says she was trying all kinds of ways to get a drink at her cousin's wedding, on Saturday, too. She knew when he brought back a drink of non-alcoholic punch for her and then she wanted one with alcohol.

Wendy goes with Tom for a few weeks to Qualicum Beach on Vancouver Island in British Columbia, where his parents live now. We enjoy a lull in activities around the house. It gives me time to put the finishing touches to "Health and Healing."

Journal Entry: May 21, 1988

Yesterday I took Bob and Doug out for lunch in the sun at a restaurant overlooking the river. We talked a little about Wendy and also about them. It was great to be there with my two handsome and thoughtful younger sons. I've missed being with them. Bob is full of energy, is being sought by two companies for work and is feeling the power of being good at his job. Doug is aware that he must pass the competency exam to get back to university if he is ever to get anywhere. They were both good company for me. It was a gorgeous day, budding poplars, blue skies, fluffy white clouds, greening grass, apple blossoms all over town. It felt so good to have time to spend with them both. I wore a red cotton sleeveless sun dress in which the loss of eleven pounds makes me feel better. It was a sunny time.

Journal Entry: May 22. 1988

I am sitting on the deck in the perfect sun, perfect temperature and perfect no bugs. Thoughts of Wendy are with me. This morning they were about her childishness. Do she and Tom have a sexual relationship or is that a "naughty" idea for her? Then the comment I often hear. "Wendy's accident is a great tragedy." Both Bill and I say, "Not true! Wendy's accident is only a tragedy if we allow it to be. We must stay positive."

Wendy and Tom return and stay with us again. Wendy has appointments for speech therapy several times a week but is impatient to learn more quickly. We tape words for her to play on her tape recorder to listen to in the night. Her speech therapist tapes words, sentences and phrases. Wendy repeats them. We have cards with words. Wendy and I do an hour together each morning at the dining room table.

First simple sounds, one-year old, two-year old sounds. The beginnings of communication. Searching for sounds she can say. Watching the mouth and the tongue.

My mouth, aaa. Her mouth, aaa. My mouth, ooo. Her mouth, ooo. My mouth, eee. Her mouth, eee. My mouth, le. Her mouth, le. Sounds, sounds, sounds. It is hard for her to make the sounds. She cannot always tell that she has not made them. It is as though she cannot hear them. Her left ear drum was dislodged in the accident. She is having it operated on later in the summer. But she can hear. She just cannot always repeat. She tries and tries anyway.

Now, eee. Now, ooo. Now, iii. Now, shhh. Now, bbb, bee, bi, bo, boo, ba, bu.

Then words. Playground words. Kindergarten words. Grade one words. Cat. Dog. Eat. Sit. Look. See. Run. Go. Come. She doesn't get it. We try again. We sit facing one another making our mouth sounds.

The sun outside calls us to the garden, but we sit with our lesson for the hour, me trying to slow down to her primitive level, me trying not to remember that we did this before, years before when she was only one and I was twenty-eight. Now she is twenty-eight and struggles to get her tongue and lips and cheeks around these sounds, these vowels, these consonants.

Her concentration is slipping. She can't do any more. She is exhausted. We let it go for today.

We need to make appointments with the doctor who is going to reattach her ear drum, the Brain Injury Follow-up Clinic and the neurologist, who can balance her medications. Wendy needs to see the dentist regularly now because Dilantin has side effects on the gums that must be monitored.

I organize the paper work of her life: applications for Assured Income for Severely Handicapped, Government of Canada Disability Pension Forms, finding additional programs for speech therapy for aphasia, recording material for the coming trial, writing letters to tidy up the details of her former life, finding where she had applied for jobs before her accident, finding her bank accounts, finding insurance forms, applying for benefits.

I start a new filing system using pink folders. For my girl. They have titles like "Insurance". "Lawyer". "Bank Accounts". "Brain Injury Information". "Medical Information". "Receipts for expenses".

Wendy needs help with her social life too. She makes dates with friends but is unable to tell them where she lives. She cannot understand what time they have agreed to meet. She gets me to phone them to check times and places. She has taken her bicycle somewhere to be fixed. She does not have a receipt of where, or when it is to be ready. Can I find it? She has a dentist appointment. Can I arrange the time and find someone to take her or can I take her myself?

Wendy hates this dependency. She is frustrated and angry that she must ask for so much help. She hates her life. She is bored staying with us, and she is tired all the time. She can't sleep. Other side effects of Dilantin are insomnia and mental confusion. It is extra hard for her to concentrate. She can't focus. The brain injury makes her drowsy. She tries to nap but she can't sleep.

We sit down to lunch but she begins to cry. Reasoning with her does not help. When she is tired like this she doesn't understand my words. Her pretty face frowns in puzzlement. Her body, still thin, hunches against this not understanding. She says "bad."

"Bad."

"Live. Bad."

"No Tom."

I try more words to reassure her. I tell her she is doing wonderfully well. That she is incredible! That I am proud of her. That she has such a dogged drive to go on, that I admire all her efforts. She understands the general idea of what I am saying but it does not pacify her. She knows how limited her life is. She knows she is not where she was last summer, in the wilderness with Tom. She wants to be part of that world again.

She becomes angry. She doesn't want to be with me. She wants to be with Tom. I don't understand what she is trying to say.

She weeps again, forgetting lunch.

I reassure. I plead. I get mad. Then I, too, weep for her struggle. She is angry that I am angry. It is her place to be angry, not mine. She says that I do not understand. Her life is useless. She lets me know by a few guttural half-words that her life is not worth living.

She pantomimes that she is going to shoot herself. She pushes herself away from the table, lurching away in anger.

I freeze. I know she knows how to do it. Her gun and shells are in the attic just off the front hall. She only needs to go into the garage, get the ladder, put it up against the wall, climb up, find and load her gun and shoot herself.

Is it really possible this is happening? Adrenalin kicks into my blood stream. I am ready to fly to stop her, but I make a decision that I will not. I don't think she really wants to do this. I will sit where I am and let her experience her terrible pain. I will not plead with her or respond to her dreadful threat.

I close my eyes, head in my hands, straining to listen. She reaches the hall. There is silence. What is she doing? Where is she now? Is she tiptoeing to get the ladder? She has to go past the kitchen door to the garage for the ladder. I can see that doorway. She does not go by. I hold my breath.

The silence continues. I sit in our sunny, white and blue dining room, utterly still, waiting for a sound. For more information.

Long minutes pass.

Then I hear crying in the hall. Soft muffled crying. Wendy, my beloved daughter, crying by herself.

I hurry to find her, huddled on the floor, head in her arms, sobbing at her hopeless situation, sobbing out her inability to understand what is now. Sobbing for Tom, for herself and for all the sadness in the world.

I kneel in front of her. I am crying too. It is worth weeping large amounts of tears for the loss of her life as she had it. She is twenty-eight years old. A university graduate. A career woman who had wonderful job possibilities. She loves a man with whom she wishes to share her life. She doesn't want to spend days learning "e" and "a" and "o" again with her mum; being dependent.

I cry for myself too. Watching my daughter in such awful pain. I don't want to be teaching her baby words over again either. I've done it once. It's not fair to have to do it again. It's too hard to be the butt of her anger, her blame, censure and bitterness. It is just too terrible. I want her well and working, happy and living with Tom, fulfilling her life's dreams.

We cry on for a little while longer and then we get up and clear away the lunch dishes and get on with the day.

It has been six months since her accident.

Journal Entry: June 22, 1988

Wendy is galloping with words these days. She counted to twenty nine yesterday. She said, "Aunty Anne!" She can say, "Honey!" "Hi, Honey!" so she called Tom to try it on him. She can say "Hurry."

Yesterday was a big day. She went over to visit our neighbour at nine. Then speech therapy at ten. Visited other patients until eleven forty. Then back to the bank and finally lunch.

Then Wendy wanted to buy flowers for Dr. Allen, as his daughter Susan, her friend, was picking her up at one. We could buy the flowers right where we had lunch, but no, Wendy wanted our friend Roy, the florist to arrange them. So we back-tracked there and she took ages to choose a bouquet. She was so right to have insisted as he made up a beautiful package for her. When Susan saw them she immediately said, "Wendy, you should present them to him yourself." So Wendy phoned Dr. Allen at the hospital, found him at a neurosurgery clinic and gave them to him between patients. (Wish I had been there!)

I've noticed that when Wendy wakes, she stays very fuzzy in her thinking for a long time. The other day we were going out for dinner. She had been snoozing and she woke and dressed in her short, blue mini-skirt dress, a long slip coming out from underneath and was climbing into woolly, bulky, winter pantyhose. She chooses some very inappropriate clothes and must be re-taught what to wear and how to colour co-ordinate, especially when she is tired or has just wakened, like yesterday.

Journal Entry: June 25, 1988

My brother Jim, and his wife Kiki are here. They added some days to their Kananaskis holiday so that they could come to see Wendy. They are thrilled with what they see.

Tom is back!

Tonight I show my last rehearsal of the slide show before going to Regina. I am pleased with it. My shoulder is in a sling and quite sore as I dislocated it yesterday. Thank goodness Tom is coming with us to help me drive the van. He is quietly fabulous. Low-key, but attentive to details for Wendy and for me.

We set off in Vanessa Van. I lie down, or Wendy lies down as we travel. It is a nice arrangement. We camp on the way. Wendy and I are billeted with the speakers in student residence rooms at the University of Regina. Tom stays in the van.

I have been coming to NAPA's Camera Canada College for many years so I have many friends attending. We find one another, renew acquaintances and choose which talks and demonstrations we will attend.

The second day, I am scheduled to speak twice: morning and afternoon, in a classroom. When the projectors are set, I check the fade/dissolve and the sound system. People wander in finding seats. It is hot and airless in the room. I am nervous. Wendy and Tom sit quietly in the back of the room. She smiles and gives me the thumbs-up sign. The room fills and the clock ticks to the hour.

I begin. I explain that the show has four parts. The first section is a collection of slides illustrating dis-ease. I have blended a rock music piece by The Who called "Can You See The Real Me, Doctor," a jarring, jagged, ragged, too-loud piece with images of the greenish neon lights inside West Edmonton Mall, child hookers, bump cars, tanks, guns, nuclear sites and fighter jets. When these slides and music combine, I feel uneasy, unwell, unsettled.

The second section has no music. The sequence illustrates the eight colours of the spectrum and I tell of my research on the effects of each colour on people. Abruptly the screen goes black. I tell the audience about Wendy's accident. The slides come back. We follow her from coma to the present. There are images of the seats outside Intensive Care, the machines which keep her alive, her bandaged head, her eyes swollen shut and visitors around her bed. I show images of her sitting: vacant, vacuous, blank, while people talk with her. There are slides of her sitting on her hospital bed, red S-scar seared across her shaven skull while visitors laugh with her, images of her kneeling and standing for the first time in physiotherapy, learning to balance. I show her with speech therapists, learning sounds, saying words, relearning how her mouth should move. I show her walking with Tom, being home with her dog for the first time, learning to blow on her flute. The section ends with Wendy in the out-of-doors, riding a horse, making a camp fire, walking in nature.

The third part is light and funny, humour in healing. Heather Bishop's silly children's song, "Belly Button, Belly Button," is a perfect fit with baby belly buttons, men's hairy belly buttons, young women's smooth skinned belly buttons, old women's baggy-skinned belly buttons and men's fat poking-out belly buttons. I have photographed belly buttons beside gall bladder scars, children with their fingers in their belly buttons and a strawberry in Bob's belly button with a little parsley for colour.

The final section is accompanied by an elegantly smooth, quiet rendition of Beethoven's "Moonlight Sonata" with a selection of images which slip through the spectrum of colours from red, orange and yellow, through green, blue, violet, indigo and finally to pure white. This is my healing piece, the piece which soothes the pain of watching my daughter's terrible struggle. It calms me. It comforts and consoles me.

It is over. The audience is still. They are stunned. They are photographers on holiday. They did not know they would be seeing such reality when they filed into this room.

Slowly the lights come on. Wendy is alone. Tom has gone. She stands up and applauds. She starts a standing ovation. I see only Wendy. I ask her to come onto the stage with me. People keep applauding. Some are crying. Some are filled with amazement. They are thrilled to see her. It is so reassuring to know she is here, real, well, walking down the stairs, smiling her wonderful smile, hugging me in front of all these people. The audience applauds and applauds. They stay standing, rejoicing with us, full of wonder at what they have just seen.

People gather around, asking questions. Wendy answers in her halting, few words. I finish what she cannot say. They congratulate us on this powerful slide show. They are touched and moved. The show is a success. Later the organizers ask me if I would move into an amphitheatre for the afternoon. They have heard that many more people will want to see it.

For the rest of the conference, everyone knows Wendy. They all speak to her and congratulate her and tell her what a great job she is doing. She is a celebrity. It is valuable for her to have all this affirmation.

Journal Entry: July 5, 1988

It feels good to have had the slide show go so well and to have it over. All my work was affirmed. I have created something which moved people, educated them and opened a door to greater understanding of brain injury. I am very pleased but very tired. So is Wendy. Tom drove us half way home to this campground on the prairie. He made our supper and set up a tent for himself and Wendy in the trees beside the campfire. I will sleep in Vanessa Van by myself, listening to soft Bach while I watch the stars out the window. Gentle snoring comes from the tent and I am glad they have each other.

Chapter 10

Depression

It is early July. In Edmonton we refocus on Bob and Shelley's wedding, but I have no energy. I feel tension from Tom. I am tired. I want to stop physio, stop counselling, stop exercising, stop the world. I am let down after Regina. I don't care for myself properly. I overeat. I drink. I am sad. I give up caring. Everything is too much effort. I want to be dead. From Batya, in counselling, I learn that I am detached from a very important part of myself. Coming back from Regina, I realize I am exhausted. I keep thinking about the fall when I dislocated my shoulder. My shoulder hurts, but it's only an outward symptom of the pain I have inside. I realize how unhappy I am. I think, it would be easier to die. I have so much to do and no energy to do it with.

Chaos already this morning. Wendy, needing to do her speech homework. Wendy, wanting to use the phone while I am calling to get someone to photograph the Stuttering Treatment and Research program tomorrow, because I shouldn't have accepted the job. Doug, dropping by before Bill leaves for work. Tom, phoning. Wendy wants him to fix the light in the garage. I want him to cut the hedge and trees at the side of the house. Bruce, phoning. He can get Wendy a phone number with all numbers under six. That's as high as she can count comfortably now. All these things pulling, taking time.

Journal Entry: July 17, 1988

I am camped with my van backing onto Hubbles Lake campground, close to Edmonton. I have both back doors open and can watch the red-winged blackbirds dart around the reeds here or look east across the lake where I hope to have a spectacular sunrise in the morning. Already it is worth it. The silence, the sunset, the closeness to nature is heaven. I have booked the same spot for next weekend for me and Bill.

Journal Entry: July 19, 1988

I have just returned from a shopping trip for Drive-Him-Mad lingerie for Shelley. It was fun. Shelley and I went out for dinner and talked about sexy stuff. We then both agreed that Wendy's participation in the lingerie shower the other night was more like a little girl playing dress-up rather than a young woman appraising the seductive value of beautiful lingerie. I wonder about Tom and Wendy's relationship.

I push through the heavy days. I am supposed to be contributing to the wedding supper for Bob and Shelley's Labour Day wedding. Her people are capable farm women, used to feeding huge, hungry harvest crews. I feel so inadequate.

I miss my friend, Elaine, Diane's mother, through all these months. I write her of my despair. She phones me and makes me talk about wanting to be dead, of not having the strength to go on, of my pain. She encourages me to let people know of my limitations, my weaknesses. Letting people know of my feelings of marrowlessness is the hardest thing I do. She listens. She allows. She permits me to say I don't want to have this burden now. Tom is away. Bill is at work. Wendy is with me all day. My friend hears me say I can't do all that needs to be done now. I won't. I cannot do it. I am in so much pain. It is too hard!

I begin to allow myself to say I can't. I tell Shelley I can't cook for the wedding. I cry a lot because I am so disappointed in myself. I cry with anyone who comes near me. I cry with my sister-in-law, my physiotherapist, my sons, with friends that drop in, Wendy's and mine, and finally with Bill. I cry when I cover the kitchen chairs with vinyl and discover it is the wrong colour. I cry making supper. Then I throw myself on my bed and cry some more.

I am afraid. I think, what am I afraid of? I tell Bill I am afraid. He asks, as he holds me, "Of what?" A list spews out. I am afraid that Wendy will be in another accident. I am afraid to be her caretaker. I'm afraid she is never safe. I'm afraid when she goes off by herself. I'm afraid he and I will split. I'm afraid we don't even know each other any more.

There! It is said. I didn't even know I was thinking all of these fears, but I said it. Bill hears. We both hear what I have blurted. We go to friends who do couple counselling. We never thought we would need them professionally but we decide to go to them because it will save us a lot of time. They listen well. They suggest that I think of Wendy's dangers as learning opportunities, as if she were a child. They tell Bill not to offer solutions when I am so low, and they suggest how to support me. Then, for our growing apart, they gave us three exercises: Twenty minutes of face-to-face talking with eye contact, saying positive things about one another, a twenty-minute walk, holding hands, twenty minutes of lying or sitting together trying to co-ordinate our breathing.

We go away relieved and try the exercises. Bill says, in one of our "I like" sessions, "I like that you are calmer in the last six months." I didn't think he had noticed!

We struggle on together. It is mid-August. Tom phones Wendy from northern B.C. He says to her on the phone, "The job didn't pan out Wendy. I'm coming home so when I get there, let's get married."

I am standing beside Wendy when she takes this call. A puzzled smile spreads over her face. She says the few words that she can to Tom and hangs up the phone. She points to the third finger on her left hand and I say, "He wants to get married?" and she nods her head. I wonder if she has understood correctly and decide not to get too excited until Tom gets home and we understand this completely. Wendy seems happy but confused. If this is to be, I am very happy simply because we have known Tom for such a long time and he is a good man. He has been so incredibly caring of Wendy and worked so hard, giving up so much time to be with her. I am sure it will be fine.

Tom arrives home two days later and they say yes, they do want to get married. Bill talks to Tom, saying that Tom must not do this just because he feels he should. We do not want him to regret it later. No, he is sure. He loves Wendy. They will be married in a small wedding before they go to Michigan where Tom has a job for the fall hunt. They would like to be married in Edmonton, by the river, in Emily Murphy Park. We offer a reception and lunch at the Faculty Club at the top of the hill overlooking the park. They accept.

Now, a new event to be planned after Bob and Shelley's wedding.

Journal Entry: August 11, 1988
Hubbles Lake again. I came out here again to think. It is very still here tonight. I paddled about in the stillness of the evening enjoying my canoe which Doug brought out for me. I am early to bed after a vegetable supper.

Journal Entry: August 13, 1988
Woke at six with pink, fluffy clouds reflected in the still lake. I got out on the lake in the canoe as quickly as I could and saw the sun rise

through the mist with a loon in the foreground. I followed a beaver into the little bay and was rewarded with a great slap of alarm as he dove. Two loons have just surfaced, twenty feet from my campfire and are gently drifting. A female red-winged blackbird is on the canoe. I've seen a great blue heron, grebes and ducks. I wonder how they survive the people.

Journal Entry: August 16, 1988

I still keep thinking I'd rather be dead. It would be so much easier. Life is hard for me these days. Yet, my back pain isn't as bad as it used to be. My neck pain goes hand-in-hand with my depression. Being depressed does not lend itself to making the extra effort which seems to be needed all around me. Just getting through each day is a major undertaking.

Two days ago, I asked Wendy if she could dig the carrots for me. The garden has not been cultivated and is mud and solid earth. I suggested she get the fork. She came back with a spade. So I said, "No, Wen," and demonstrated a fork with my fingers. She went off, and I saw her get a rake (Just like fingers!) So I left what I was doing and went with her to the garden to find the fork and demonstrated the first dig, then washing the carrots with the hose. She kind of clicked into recognition and then did the task very happily. I keep forgetting she must be re-taught so many things.

Chapter 11

The Weddings

Bob and Shelley are married in Mistaya Canyon, near Saskatchewan River Crossing in Banff National Park on the hottest Labour Day on record. It is three great days in the mountains, filled with happy people and joy. Wendy and Tom are there with all the rest of the family. We have some fun. My mood lifts.

When we come home, Wendy tells me that she and Tom have set October 1st for their wedding. Bob and Shelley's wedding reception is October 2nd and my first One Woman Photography Show is October 5th. How can I do this? I say, "Wendy, that's a terrible day. There is so much going on!" and she looks at me with her evil eye, and says, "It's my day." I pause and say, "Yes my darling, it is your day, and it's only a wedding. Let's do it! What can we do to help?"

I have two heirloom dresses of my paternal grandmothers. One of them, an exquisite short lace sheath, slips over Wendy's shoulders and falls into an elegant, simple, wedding dress, perfect with a delicate slip underneath and modest accessories. She will wear flowers in her hair by Roy.

The preparations for Tom and Wendy's wedding are simple. We invite our families and some friends. What we don't realize is that

Wendy wants everyone to come. We actually photocopy some of the wedding invitations because Wendy keeps giving them away. She doesn't remember who is coming. We decide it is not important. We will just enjoy the day and not worry about details.

Journal Entry: September 10, 1988

Bill and I do more marriage work. The counsellors say a good marriage is like a lawn which needs constant care. The events of the last four years; moving house, Bill's job search, Grampie's death, Wendy's accident, my starting a new job and the weddings all add up to tremendous changes and stress. They suggest a special time each week just for one another. I am pleased to think of a date with Bill once a week.

Journal Entry: September 15, 1988

Wendy has been here for two days. It is fun! I am managing my time with her better and she continues to improve. Her computer lesson went well yesterday, the best yet.

About the wedding. So far, no music! So when Uncle Ted, my younger brother and Wendy's godfather who is going to give the toast to the bride, phoned last night from Toronto we suggested that he and Aunty Dinah be responsible for training a choir of guests in five minutes for "Here Comes The Bride". We're having lots of laughs about the casualness of this wedding.

Wendy has used or squirrelled away all the wedding invitations. There are all kinds of new names in her book. Has she asked them to the wedding? We probably won't know until the day. So Bill is going to photocopy the one we have left! What a riot!

Journal Entry: September 18, 1988

A windy, cold, sunny Sunday. The children are really leaving us by ourselves. It is wonderful to be alone in our house. We had a great idea! Lend the van to Tom and Wendy to go to Michigan.

Journal Entry: September 23, 1988

It has been strenuous having Wendy here and discovering, after a day, that Tom is away for three days!

Journal Entry: September 26, 1988

Living with Wendy is emotionally, psychologically and physically draining. Friday she "polished" her dark brown boots with a light tan polish. She tried to fix the fence by cutting some boards with hedge clippers! She put lemon oil on the furniture but didn't understand about wiping it off. When I came home yesterday though, and found the cake tin full of chocolate cookies that she made, I was happy. A great breakthrough.

We left her to get to the Glenrose Hospital by herself. She walked up to the bus stop and caught the wrong bus. By chance, she sat beside a nurse, who got off with her and phoned a cab so Wen finally got to her appointment. It illustrates the thousands of things she has to learn but also her resourcefulness to correct things herself while on her own.

Journal Entry: September 28, 1988

Wendy appeared before breakfast with a letter she had written years ago about her Grampie and she wanted me to read it to her. She wept so hard that he is gone. She loved him so much. Then I read aloud her own last letter to me, about mother/daughter relationships. We cried some more and said yesterday had been a bad, bad day for both of us. I had been angry with her for not coming home by bus like she told me she would. I was worried because we had to go to a funeral. Today she is very tired. We cried some more. Then Wendy had an appointment with Dr. Aung. No time for my meditation or bath. Went shopping for some dressy pants to wear to the wedding, went to the Alberta Motor Association for maps and insurance, then to the bank to find Wendy's lost funds. No luck!

Later the doorbell rang constantly. Gifts, friends, deliveries, and visitors. Wendy has an upset stomach, diarrhea, can't eat and she looks awful. Bill put Wendy to bed and he and I walked down to the river.

Bruce arrived and suggested that we sing our family's grace at the wedding lunch. Everyone loves Bruce. He has creative ideas! He is going to have copies made of the words. He is going to be the Master of Ceremonies. Good choice. Tall, bearded, gentle man, who is innately funny.

I polish the teak furniture, smelling the woody, pungent smell of the teak oil on an old T-shirt rag, smoothing it across the dining room table top, pressing hard, working the oil into the elegant wood, polishing it with long strokes, following the grain. I am stilled by this mundane task of rubbing simple furniture. The physical work uses a little of my frantic, excess energy and calms me. I rearrange some flowers, taking joy in this peaceful artistic endeavour. I am trying to keep calm as Wendy's wedding day approaches.

A day of hope and joy, October 1, 1988. Ten months after that terrible crash of metals in the winter's night. It is Wendy and Tom's wedding day.

It is early. We wake slowly on our pillows. Wendy comes quietly into our room, obviously very unhappy. We are instantly alert.

"What is it, Wendy? Why are you so sad?"

"I . . not. . . nice . . person." she says, haltingly.

"Not. . . nice,"

Our hearts are pierced. This is her wedding day!

Her self esteem is non-existent. We reassure. We encourage. We say how wonderful she is, how much we love her. How much Tom loves her. How much everyone loves her.

I remember I have a string of creamy white pearls for her wedding keepsake, a mother's gift to a cherished, beautiful, special, only daughter for her wedding day. I find them and give them to her saying that when she wears them, anytime, she is to know she is loved, no matter how she feels about herself. These pearls are to be tangible proof that she is loved. No matter what day, what place, what time she puts them on in the future, she is to know that she is loved.

She understands the intent, is distracted and cries happy tears.

The house is full of flowers. Garlands decorate the black wrought-iron railing outside the front door. Diamond willow with pink roses and white baby's breath twine up the stone fireplace. There is a tall, elegant arrangement on the long, teak sideboard.

Gifts are delivered. The doorbell ushers in the people. Wendy's Winnipeg school friend, Lorraine is doing the photography; Tom's sister, beautiful, blond Lydia, make-up sales representative, is doing Wendy's make up and her hair. Wendy's lawyer-friend, Barb, arrives. She is to be her Best Gal. Lots of laughter comes from the bathroom as these friends gather around Wendy on this joyous occasion. She puts on the floral crown of tiny baby's breath gathered with ecru lace ribbon at the back of her head with three pink roses. She looks lovely. She is smiling. She is enchanting.

Best man, uncles, aunts, brothers and friends all arrive to do their part. Great Aunty Kit, ninety, has come from Ontario. She is elegantly dressed, hair freshly done, leaning on her slim black cane. She is captivated with the way Wendy looks and tells Wendy that she remembers wearing similar dresses in the nineteen-twenties.

The day is windless, cool and cloudy, saturating the yellows, rusts and oranges of the trees against the grey green of the North Saskatchewan River. The air smells fresh and woody.

Tom and Wendy face one another in the park, supported by

their attendants. Guests gather around, standing under the trees in the clearing. There is a hush as everyone waits to hear Wendy utter the words "I do," the only words she needs to say. She does, very quietly, but her words are clear. Tom watches her carefully and supports her with his smile and his merry eyes.

They are married.

At The Faculty Club, overlooking the river valley, there is a brief reception line while one of Bob's friends plays his flute. There is much rejoicing. Lots of smiles and laughter as we celebrate this wedding.

Great Aunty Kit is given a special seat for lunch. Everyone else just takes a place. Bruce, master of ceremonies, leads us all in singing the family grace,

Thank you God for the world so sweet

Thank you God for the food we eat.

Thank you God for the birds that sing.

Thank you God for everything.

A main course of cold salmon, green peas, tomatoes, and salad is followed by chocolate pecan pie.

The best man makes an emotional toast to Wendy. There is a great standing ovation with lots of tears around the room recognizing the efforts of this courageous young couple. A toast to the groom follows. Tom stands to answer the toast. Always a man of few words, he smiles at his bride, says that she is the one who likes to talk and gives her the microphone. Again a standing ovation. Wendy makes us all laugh by giving stuffed bears to her dad and the best man. Then Uncle Ted makes a wonderful short toast to the bride. He and Dinah sing "Amazing Grace' with words which they have made up for the occasion.

A fairy-story ending is happening after these long months of struggle. "Happily ever after" is our wish for this unique young couple.

Chapter 12

Fall of 1988, Michigan

Wendy and Tom go to Michigan where he will be guiding. They stay at Blue Lake Lodge where all the guides stay. The guides go off in the early morning and Val looks after the lodge. Wendy stays with her. We assume that Tom is coping well. I go back to work at the Worker's Compensation Board Rehabilitation Centre. We worry about money. Bill's income is lower than my part-time pay some months and things are financially serious for us. I have no journal entries about Wendy for a full month, so we have a little time to return our lives to normal.

Then Wendy is found unconscious in a ditch. A call comes to Bill's office, the Medic Alert bracelet contact, from a hospital in Michigan. The nurse is worried that Wendy is unable to tell them who she is and where she lives. We reassure her that the brain injury was from another time. We tell them Tom's name, address, and phone number. He gets to the hospital where Wendy tells him she was on her way to the post office on her bike, had an awful headache and got off her bike and sat down. She has been neglecting her Dilantin.

Wendy goes back to Blue Lake Lodge and we begin to be in phone contact with Val. She is glad to talk to us about Wendy and said she didn't call earlier as Wendy doesn't want people talking about her. Val is incredibly good about looking after Wendy while Tom is at work.

Tom finishes his job and they drive back from Michigan. On the way back, on November 15, Wendy calls us and says slowly and carefully, "Hello . . Mr. . . Math . . ew . . son." She had said "Mathewson" a half an hour before and Tom said, "Call your Dad, Wendy and tell him." The first time she had said her name for almost a year.

Tom and Wendy decide to live here in Edmonton until next summer. They stay with us while they look for a place to rent. They both expect that I am available to Wendy. Things are different now that I am back at work. I am not heard again in needing to know when she will be here and when she will not. It makes a difference to my planning. I am not as flexible now because I am at work. I thought Tom understood.

Wendy starts outpatient speech therapy at the Glenrose. She will see Dr. Aung, Dr. Allen, Dr. Low, speech therapy, hematology, and reactivate the Community Enrichment Program at Grant MacEwan Community College.

I am again confronted by Wendy's deficits. She forgets that I gave her my work phone number, that she and Tom have a microwave oven, and that she can't take a bus yet. These are serious problems. Tom says her spirit was broken for five or six days after the seizure. I see remnants of that loss of confidence. I think I have to change myself and not want to do so much for her.

Chapter 13

The Second Year

Wendy's lack of comprehension and memory, her lack of organizational skills mean that she double books appointments, loses papers with telephone numbers or addresses, forgets about meetings, and is severely disorganized. Whoever she is living with spends inordinate amounts of time mopping up the details of her life.

Journal Entry: January 27, 1989
Wendy was mad at Tom. She swam thirty laps at the pool. She then slept here for a while and when I got home, she was still groggy. She needed to show me letters to Aunty Kit and a needlepoint gift she had made at the Glenrose and all manner of things. She has broken the clasp on her pearls again. I wasn't getting what she was trying to tell me and she got very angry and shouted "FUCK" into the cupboard and then turned around and began trying again. What a woman!.

Living with Wendy is demanding, her needs immediate. Please, can I read her mail? Please, can I help her answer it? Can I explain what it means? Please, can I talk to someone else on the phone? Everything needs to be RIGHT NOW. I feel so bad for her, that she needs so much help, that I want to help her immediately but it is time consuming. Also it is a constant game of charades, guessing at what she means. She phones someone and is not able to understand what they are saying, so she finds me and asks for help. I have no idea who is on the other end of the phone, what they are trying to plan, and why Wendy needs help, so it takes a little detective work to find out. When we get the details straight I must write them down and then, after saying goodbye, spend time with Wendy clarifying what the person on the phone has said and why that was significant. Then, having returned to whatever work I had interrupted, there soon comes another request because another phone call is in progress.

Wendy plans to meet someone on Thursday but Wendy understands Wednesday. She plans to have coffee at 101 Street when the person means 110 Street. She thinks they say seven o'clock when they actually say nine o'clock.

Wanting to help is easy. Having the energy to respond to her multiple needs for eighteen hours a day is hard. Then, if limits are set, and I say, "I can't help because I need to have a bath," guilt pounces, because she is so dependent. While I am unable to attend to her needs she can't do anything. She can't watch TV, or read a book, or listen to the radio, as none of it makes any sense. What can she do in the meantime?

If she raged, pouted or was furious, it would be different, but she is unaware of how her needs interrupt my life. She is unable to check herself from asking, driven by her constant need to know, to understand, to comprehend. I admire this tenacity.

It is time to have some medical follow-up. There is a new outpatient Brain Injury Clinic at the Glenrose Hospital. Wendy has never been seen there. She has never been seen or referred to anyone since she left the Glenrose in April 1988. So eighteen months after the injury, almost a year after her discharge from the Glenrose, we go to the clinic for a doctor appointment. The doctor asks us both questions. I answer that Wendy has a lot of difficulty speaking and understanding. I tell her that we need to be careful about where she goes as she gets lost, makes mistakes and forgets things. This is the full report from that appointment:

Brain Injury Clinic.
March 1989

Severe head injury. Has dysphasia, both receptive and expressive.

Wendy also exhibits some cognitive impairment especially vis-à-vis short term memory.

Needs supervision and monitoring etc. when she travels outside her home.

This is not news to us! Nor is it helpful.

Journal Entry: March 17, 1989
Bill and I went to Wendy's lawyer, Rob Graesser, with her yesterday. She was quite articulate, getting her points across. She handled herself beautifully and made point after point talking to him even though she had to write or demonstrate. It was amazing to watch the superhuman effort she makes for strangers. She is extraordinary! I watch with admiration.

Tom and Wendy go out to Vancouver Island in the early spring. They live in a motel, close to Tom's parents at Qualicum Beach.

Tom becomes quiet and morose. Wendy tells us he spends the day lying on the bed, in the motel, doing nothing, just staring at the ceiling. His parents live just a few blocks away but we don't hear from them that anything is wrong. I am sure they are sad watching their son in such depressed spirits.

The months pass with struggles for both Tom and Wendy. Tom is trying to deal with the loss of his old Wendy, with his loss of independence, with his being needed round the clock for so many things Wendy would never have asked of him before.

Wendy wants to find a speech therapist in Qualicum Beach, but there doesn't seem to be one. The closest is an hour and a half away. Tom says he will drive her but she says she doesn't want to go. There seems to be nothing for either of them to do all day. Eventually Wendy attends art classes with the senior Kehoes.

Bill and I visit Wendy and Tom on Vancouver Island.

Journal Entry: Tuesday May 16, 1989. Vancouver Island.
I have been trying to get my thoughts clarified about how I find Wendy. It is hard, as I simply don't want to admit to what I see. She is slow, repetitive, vulnerable and dependent. She is very grateful for our awareness of how hard she works to talk or to do things.
"Poor dear." Bill just says. "Poor dear."
The real Wendy is there, my daughter, who I know so well. But she is hidden behind her inability to communicate. It is difficult to watch her dependency.
Tom continues to be supportive, loving and helpful. He is a kind man. He is simple and uncomplicated. He lives for today. Unfortunately his bear hunting guide job fell through. Some friends came by to ask him about joining them in Valemont, B. C. on a major hunting/guiding venture which would have future stability and development, so that is in their future.

If Wendy is going to have any rehabilitation program, it is apparent she needs to live in Edmonton. Both she and Tom prefer living in the country but the reality is that Wendy can't drive and needs to live somewhere near a hospital where therapies take place, so she can take a bus, or walk.

While we are on Vancouver Island, Bill gets an excellent job as manager of the Wood Gundy office in Edmonton. We determine that, financially speaking, I can resign from my physiotherapy job which makes me available to Wendy. This feels right. Wendy comes to us while Tom goes to the Yukon and the Northwest Territories. We learn again to speak slowly and check that Wendy understands. Again being ready to help all the time is necessary. Wendy is frustrated, angry, weepy, exhausted. We try a Reading Learning Centre. She is challenged but fades with fatigue.

It is mid-afternoon, hot and sunny. I am working in the kitchen cutting celery, making a potato salad for supper. Wendy has gone for a walk in the ravine behind our house.

The doorbell rings. Wendy is on the step with a strange man. She says, "He wants to talk...to...you."

The man says, "I felt you needed to know that you have to look after your daughter better. She is very friendly. She came up to me in the ravine where I was looking at a map. She asked if she could help me. I know there is something wrong with her, but I could have done anything, you know. She is too friendly."

"I know that she is friendly," I say to him, "but you could tell her that yourself."

He turns to her and says, "Wendy, you shouldn't talk to strange men, especially in the ravine where there is no help around."

Wendy thanks him and I thank him for his interest. I am beginning to learn that people speak to the caregivers of people with disabilities, not to the people themselves. I am also aware that Wendy always has been friendly, has always spoken to strangers that looked as though they needed help. She has good judgement about people, and I am not worried about her.

I make an appointment with the Northern Alberta Brain Injury Society, (NABIS) to find out how they can help us. They offer support services and information about brain injury.

Wendy visits Metis Beach, Quebec, for a month. There is a grand, old Mathewson summer house on Eagle Point on the St. Lawrence River where Aunty Anne is spending the summer. Wendy causes all kinds of uproar and expensive long distance calls. She isn't happy in Metis. She loses her wallet, including credit cards, for the third time! Tom phones her from B.C. He misses her!

I go to the Brain Injury Relearning Centre in Calgary to put in an application for Wendy to attend if she is accepted. The major problem with the Centre is there is no residential program. Where would she live? Who should she live with? Tom? Us? A residence?

Journal Entry: July 27, 1989

Tom is in town. He said to Bill yesterday that he realized that he can't "do it alone" any more. That he has spent almost two years with Wendy and he can't do it by himself. He thought that he could. I was touched by his admission.

The amount Wendy has to relearn is still enormous.

Journal Entry: August 1, 1989

Wendy is here now and I am committed to being her health care co-ordinator for the next two months. Tom has said he can't do it alone and I am sure that I can't either, but I can work hard at checking out all the resources available for Wendy. I will commit myself to staying clear about what the goals are here. Independence for Wendy. Independent living. The three priorities we set yesterday.

1. Taking the medication.

2. Eating regularly.

3. Learning about money.

Wendy's days are full of self-doubt and frustration. She is quite depressed. She is losing her confidence but not her grit or determination. She is angry, really angry at the car accident and it's effects. She is angry with me because I keep checking to see if she really can do the things she says she is going to do. But I think she is using her anger to show me she can do things. I think that is beneficial.

She rides her bike to an exercise program planned especially for her at the University of Alberta. We buy books on brain learning and vitamins and mineral supplements for insomnia. When we meet in the morning, she has been up for ages, planning her day. We organize her desk. By night it is chaos again but she has found the addresses and names for at least twelve promotional letter mail-outs for Tom's business so she can help him. Her days are often whirlwinds of activity. Today she had a hair appointment, a speech therapy session, an early evening with Lydia at a wedding shower, and a dinner with Bruce's family. It is hard for me to keep up with her normal pace, but she needs to keep busy. It is probably not more than she would do, had she not had the accident, and I so want "normal" for her. So I help as much as I can to assist her with all these activities.

I pick up an application form for an aphasia program in Michigan. I get Wendy's résumé from a niece who has it on her computer.

Journal Entry: August 13, 1989
Wendy went off to Valemont by bus on Thursday so I have been solitary. I love it! I spent two hours on Friday night cleaning and sorting Wendy's room again and another two hours yesterday, clearing all my stuff out so Wendy will be able to have more room for her own belongings at our house. I hate throwing anything out because she uses concrete things to demonstrate her speech, like bringing us a

photograph if she wants to tell who she wants to contact, or finding an old letter with a reference to an event she wants to go to. Her creativity is amazing.

Journal Entry: August 14, 1989

Wendy and I had a terrible morning, crying, fighting and making up, blaming and fighting from 9 until 11.30 mostly about her living here. It was exhausting. I gather she and Tom had the same kind of weekend. She is fighting mad at everything. Having Wendy say she hated Tom was the breaker for me. She hasn't said that before. She is miserable and unhappy. She goads me. I bite.

She raged, "I should have died." I shouted back, "The bad news is that you didn't." She took a moment to comprehend what I had said and she was shocked. Then she started to laugh and then we both laughed but oh, how true I feel that sentiment is today. She should have died!

My worst thought is that her life won't get any better. Her anger may go on forever. Then I remember that she, too, worked on anger today. I asked her if she wanted counselling after she said she hated Tom and she said yes. I said, "NABIS, or the University?" "University." She got an appointment. So she did act. She wants all this anger to stop too.

Wendy is exhausted. She goes from 6 AM to midnight every day. She still doesn't sleep, which makes her nasty all the time. This morning she was furious that I had not found a computer school for her last year. Then we were in a free-for-all shouting match. We said awful things to one another.

Doug says I am the wrong person to be with Wendy. I am angry and sad. I cannot stay uninvolved. I love her with the love of a lioness and I will fight furiously for her survival.

Journal Entry: August 21, 1989

Hubbles Lake in Vanessa Van. My eyes are red from weeping. My head feels as though there is a vice pushing in at the crown. However, the sky was a gentle grey and pink as I drove out relieving the pressure. The beach is clean, the ducks still paddle about and there is relative silence. No interruptions. No angry Wendy. To continue the metaphor I often use of comparing Wendy's recovery to a marathon for which I have had no training, today, I hit the wall. There is real pain. A recognition that there is no one else who can do this for me. Where is the finish line of this everlasting marathon?

Wendy's legal claim is about putting a dollar figure on all this pain and suffering. What a joke. There isn't enough money in the world to compensate for all this pain.

Wendy is so difficult to live with it is almost impossible to document. I am manipulated beyond imagining. I am in tears four to eight times a day. It is horrible.

Wendy has become devious, not taking her L-triptithon for sleeping, not being on time, not going swimming or bicycling to exercise. When I told her that her behaviour exhausted me, that she is 29 and I am 56 and can't handle it, she said Tom says the same thing.

Now she doesn't like me showing Health and Healing. She was asked to speak on a panel for NABIS. She doesn't want to, as a future boss out there might see it and know that she had been in an accident, had a brain injury and not hire her. Now "everyone" knows about her.

Some friends drop away. She cries because she says she hasn't any friends any more.

Journal Entry: September 5, 1989

Wendy was awake until 4:30 AM worrying about why Tom has not phoned her. She has phoned Valemont five times. She went to Valemont today because Tom needs her. Before she left, Wendy asked Mairead if she thinks that Tom has a girl friend. Mairead said "Of course not!"

Wendy says that Tom got really angry asking, "Are we ever going to have fun again?"

And so, knowing she needed to exercise, Wendy biked off to her speech therapy, trying to pedal off the hurt, sadness and frustration.

Oh! The wound of watching a daughter suffer so.

Journal Entry: September 15, 1989

I just saw a young woman on television playing the flute and I burst into tears as I remembered Wendy, calmly, confidently, awaiting her cue, taking a breath, and blowing sweet notes into her own flute so many times. I remembered Wendy practicing her flute in the old house, beside the fireplace. I remember the many concerts we have attended: Pigeon Lake summer music camp, junior high concert band, Balmoral Hall's graduation exercises. All with Wendy, catching our eye, knowing we were there in the audience, applauding her efforts.

Wendy was on television this morning for Brain Injury Awareness Week. She was not as relaxed as she was at the press conference for NABIS on Monday but she did a great job. Apparently Tom phoned here, spoke at some length to Bill and said he appreciates what we are doing. It is nice to know we have his support.

Wendy visits her old scuba diving friend, Judy Henderson, for a few days at Pigeon Lake. They had, before Wendy's accident, done several dives together, some in Jasper on an advanced, deep diving course, and others, just for fun at the Lester B. Pearson College off Vancouver Island. They are good friends.

When I pick up Wendy, I ask Judy how she is able to deal with Wendy's anger. Judy says, very simply, that she and her brothers felt they lost their mother and father when her older sister broke her neck and became a quadriplegic. She tells me her parents spent all their time with the sister, like Bill and I are spending all our time and energy with

Wendy. Judy understands Wendy's anger because she says her sister was the same, striking out in her rage at having lost so much. Judy is aware that it has nothing to do with her. She is a wise woman at a young age.

Journal Entry: September 26, 1989
I lost my cool last night, so Wendy told me to go away. I did.

Journal Entry: September 27, 1989
Normality returns briefly as Wendy took the bus to Jasper, desperate to meet Tom and be with him. Yesterday morning she was behaving badly, blaming me for many, many wrongs. Wrongs alive in her head, but trapped by her inability to gather the massive effort needed to discuss them. The final straw was that her acceptance to the Michigan School was addressed to Wendy Mathewson, not Kehoe. She raged at me, pointing to the envelope. I raged back, telling her it was not my fault they had made a mistake and she had to stop blaming me for everything that's going wrong with her life. She didn't have a monopoly on misery. It is not fun for me to watch my wonderful daughter deal with a brain injury either, and I think my life is also difficult since her accident.
We wept and cried together. She was really sobbing for the first time in a while. I told her how precious she is to me, how much I love her and how awful it is to watch her pain. She seemed sad all day. She was very good telling her needs at the Health and Healing show for the nurses at the University Hospital, but very badly behaved at the dentist's office. Her jaw was injured in the accident and might add to the legal case. There was much waiting and paperwork.

Another fall is here and Tom gets his guiding job again in Michigan. Wendy has been accepted at the Michigan School for Aphasia but it doesn't start until the end of October. They travel away in Vanessa Van again. This year, Tom and Wendy have been given a house on an isolated lake. Tom takes the van to work early in the morning and Wendy is left alone, all day. She is desperate for company, desperate for someone to talk to, for something to do. She is left alone with her thoughts which go 'round and 'round in her head, worrying and worrying an idea. It is called "perseverating" in brain injury literature. There is no resolution or help.

She phones us many times a day, desperate to talk, desperate to make contact with someone who values her, who knows her, who knows who she used to be. I talk to her, trying to make suggestions of what she can do. Who else she can phone? How will she put in her long day? No therapy, no reading help, no physical things for her to do, no destination, no company. She is frantic. She has a month to put in by herself and each day is excruciatingly long.

Journal Entry: October 15, 1989

I just woke from a dream where Wendy was being crucified, upside down. Granted we saw the movie "Jesus of Montreal" last Monday, but this tells me where my pain is about her. My psyche is working overtime. Wendy has been phoning from her lonely residence in Michigan where she is all by herself for the whole day, every day. Her torment is in trying to fill the day with no one to talk to. In the dream, Bill and I had to watch her being crucified. It was terrible.

Life goes on in spite of the pain. Wendy continues phoning. We disregard the costs as the lawyer, Rob Graesser, says it is one of the expenses we hope to recoup from the legal case. If we win! We know things will be better when she gets to the University of Michigan Residential Aphasia Program in Ann Arbor. It starts on October 30 and runs to December 12. Ann Arbor is not too far from where Tom is located. He can drive down for a day to visit Wendy.

The mission statement of the program is "to provide excellent and intensive speech and language services to our clients while contributing to the knowledge base in speech and language." We have heard that it is the best program available in the U.S. As well, I have written to the Michigan Head Injury Alliance with the hopes that someone will be available to Wendy outside of the program, for some social life apart from the school. They do not respond for weeks.

I feel terrible that Wendy is so far away and by herself.

Chapter 14

School For Aphasia, Ann Arbor, Michigan

Journal Entry: November 21, 1989

I am flying to Minneapolis/St. Paul, on my way to Detroit, to see Wendy and Tom. I am relieved that I am going.

It is now November. Wendy asked me to come to this Michigan School for Aphasia. I am glad, as I have been concerned about her. She has been here since October 30th. I fly from Edmonton, rent a car at the airport and find my way to The Sanctuary, an exclusive fenced-in property of many acres where deer are raised. In the centre of the property is a rustic, old, wood-frame lodge set in the woods. Tom picked up Wendy from the school and, being the only Canadian guide, is taking care of the lodge for the American Thanksgiving weekend.

I arrive after supper. Tom and Wendy have the master bedroom suite downstairs. I have a room upstairs. I am confused. Wendy asked me to come but is hostile at my arrival. She is furious that I am here. I don't understand, but I tell Tom and Wendy that I will find somewhere else to stay tomorrow.

There is a bar with the most incredible selection of liquor I have ever seen outside a liquor store. It is all available to us as an open bar. The lodge is for member guests only who pay huge sums to come to this enclosed, secluded piece of Michigan land. The Sanctuary is totally surrounded by a twelve foot wire fence.

I am sickened by what I see. There are feeding places for the deer with blinds hidden in the trees nearby. Hunters wait at dawn or dusk to shoot the deer as they eat the bales of hay put out for them. The hunters can be driven in cars to the blinds! I cannot believe this is what Tom calls guiding. What kind of a guide is needed at this sanctuary for hunters! But this is my son-in-law who has cared for my daughter. I think about how he has watched the woman he loves be destroyed. I am aware of the kindness of the people he is working for, who have encouraged him to come with his wife and supported him through this trying time. I've heard that he feels responsible for the accident because he was driving the car that night. He does not want Wendy to be the way she is: angry, non-comprehending, neither laughing nor loving, the way she was before. I say nothing. It is not my place to tell him I don't like what he does. I say I will go to find a motel in the morning and stay there so they can be alone. I understand Wendy's need to be alone with Tom.

In the morning Tom comes to me and says, no, under no circumstances should I go. He wants me there. I get a sense that he doesn't want to be alone with Wendy. He pleads with me to stay. I check it out with Wendy and she says yes, they have talked about it and they want me to stay. I go out to photograph the fall colours and the lake, the beautiful country-side and the lodge. This gives them some time to themselves.

Journal Entry: November 24, 1989
It seems pointless to write and re-anguish about all the hassles, the details, the imagined wrongs, the uncertainty and the sadness. Wendy finds black people ominous, hostesses at restaurants surly and

unhelpful, teachers faulty. She is petulant, critical, dissatisfied and quick to be furious, to walk out, to shut a book, to throw something across the table.

Sunday night Wendy and I leave Tom and drive into Ann Arbor where I rent a hotel room for two nights so that I can spend the day at Wendy's school with her teachers in order to understand what she is learning. Wendy and I stay together at the hotel and we drive in to the university early Tuesday morning. The teacher is late. Wendy says she is always late. When she comes, she tells me that Wendy spends the first fifteen minutes of every lesson complaining, saying she shouldn't be there. Asking why is she there? Saying the place is wrong, the curriculum is wrong, the school is wrong, the way they run it is wrong. Apparently she goes through this same ritual, every day, cleverly distracting the teacher from her purpose and from the lesson. I'm told the following hour is the same. And the next and the next. Wendy argues, becomes angry, always distracts from the lesson to talk about herself, her accident, her life, her business, her doubts, her Tom. Wendy says the teacher is wrong, the school is wrong, Tom is wrong, I am wrong.

Journal Entry: November 28, 1989

I am between planes on my way home trying to assess what I have seen. Wendy vacillates between anger and despair and then benign resignation. I think she must feel trapped. She asks Tom repeatedly. "What do you think you'll do, Tom?" "Where can we live, Tom?"
Wendy is angry with everyone. Me, for sending her here to the school; Aunty Kit, for paying; Tom, for hunting; Val, the woman who runs the Blue Lake Lodge, for not wanting her; the school, for testing her again, for NOT knowing it all. So far I think Bill is OK.
I went through her day with her yesterday at the Aphasia program. I

am dismayed. I did not realize how poorly things are going. However the staff seem positive. They all like Wendy and want to help. The group counselling, which I thought would be the place for Wendy to talk about all her personal problems is a group about speech, not about personal counselling.

At 8 AM there is a class on speech which focuses on listening and comprehending. Then nothing until eleven. Then a speech pathologist works with Wendy on sentence structure.

We went back to the residence for a big lunch around a table, a huge square table with fourteen disabled, aphasic people silently eating lunch. Most of the people here are between fifty and seventy, and have had stokes or aneurysms. Wendy is thirty. There are only two other young men with traumatic brain injuries, but they do not live in the residence so there is no one to do anything with after class.

Meals are lonely affairs, people sitting alone, each in their own agony. Self-esteem gone; confidence gone; humour gone; coping one-handedly with corn flakes or porridge or with buttering toast.

Wendy was trying hard to make meal times into recreational events by arranging the tables to allow people to visit during the meal. We had come at breakfast. Now, for lunch, Wendy saw that the tables had been returned to the old way, she was furious and stomped out of the room. The dear, black woman on kitchen duty changed things back to suit Wendy. Wendy was somewhat mollified, but it really was strange, sitting with such a silent group. I am sure the dining room has further depressed our used-to-be cheerful Wen.

We had a group speech session at 1 PM. Again, the staff was late. It consisted of two young men, Wendy and a speech pathologist, each telling of their Thanksgiving and what was in the news. Finally at three o'clock we met with Wendy's primary therapist. She experiences Wendy's anger daily because Wendy is so tired by that time of day. She put it succinctly. Wendy is standing in the way of her own concentration by being so angry. Therefore, half the therapy session is taken up with dealing with Wendy's frustrations.

Wendy is stuck in her room after class. She would like to swim or go to a music concert or a movie but she is unable to read the notices on the bulletin board of campus happenings.

I speak privately with her primary therapist, who seems to understand what is going on. She feels that Wendy has so many personal matters to work through that she is unable to take full advantage of the program. Wendy is so consumed by personal issues she asks all the teachers the same questions, with the same perseverance, day after day. "Should I have got married? Where should I live? What should I do?"

I kick myself for not coming earlier. Wendy has had seven weeks of the ten offered. Why did I think Tom would have visited with Wendy and gone over the program? I didn't realize how bored and lonely she would be. I speak again with the primary therapist and the director of the school. Yes, they will help her get out in the evenings, show her where the swimming pool is, will work more directly with her. The director tells me that the final report from their program will suggest that Wendy needs major psychological counselling and after that, to return again for a second session. They say it would be wise for Tom to be included in counselling.

I am unprepared for the second part of that evaluation. Wendy needs to return for another session? If I am unprepared, imagine how Wendy will feel! Later at the hotel, she says she will never go back. They are all terrible. It is a lousy program. I understand a little better what both sides have experienced. This brain injury business is so complex. It becomes more and more complicated and seems to go on forever. Just when we think we have found an answer, more questions follow.

Chapter 15
Winter,
1989-90

I have hardly walked in the door back home when the phone rings. It is Michigan, School for Aphasia. Someone found Wendy in her dark room in the dormitory, non-responsive. She has had a major seizure, alone. They have taken her to the hospital. They call Tom away from The Sanctuary.

The next morning we have a call from Tom. He is terse. He says, "I am shipping Wendy home on Air Canada flight #486, arriving Edmonton at 6:39 PM."

"Tom," I say, "You must be so upset."

He says little else. I can hear the lump in his throat. I read between the silences. He is desolate. In Alberta, one must be seizure free for a full year before applying for a driver's licence. He wants Wendy to be able to drive. He knows how badly she wants her independence. He knows this means another twelve-month wait for her to be able to drive.

Wendy is sent home from Michigan on the anniversary of her darkest day, November 30, two years after her accident. She hates that day. She gets off the plane dozy from the seizure, groggy, non-comprehending, dull of eye. She has regressed again. She is like a naughty, little girl that has been caught doing something bad. She doesn't want to see anyone or let anyone know she is here. Apparently she drank some Grand Marnier at The Sanctuary. Her blood level was low so she either forgot, or was lying, about taking her anti-seizure medication.

Bill and I put her to bed in "her" room. After a few days of rest and care she comes around. She begins her questions again. "What should I do?" she asks, "Where should we live? In the city or in the country? Why did I marry Tom?"

Journal Entry: November 30, 1989
It is now two years since Wendy's accident. I feel responsible for her seizure. Guilty for not getting to Michigan sooner and realizing what a terrible time she was having and trying to fix it! And I was so enjoying getting back to normal living myself. Now reality hits again.

Journal Entry: December 3, 1989.
Doug is here, seriously disabled with his back. His doctor says that 80 to 90 percent of herniated discs go away with bed rest. Three weeks of bed rest please, so I'm glad to have him here. He is in the room upstairs. Wendy downstairs. Our artist friends, Pam and Sandy, are back, staying with us for the Art Fair. Uncle Jim Tremain came last evening while Bill and I were out at a noisy company dinner and dance. We have a full house.

Journal Entry: December 14, 1989
I was invited to sit on the board of NABIS. Wendy has a bee in her bonnet about me giving up my job and now my job is NABIS. Brain injury!
Bill and I went out with friends to the movies. We got home to find Doug with swollen eyes and sniffly nose, having just had a big

emotional time with Wendy. It is good to have him here, although it is hard to watch him, bent over in pain, when he is up. I got him a second batch of Percodan yesterday. The doctor is going to operate. He may get a bed in the hospital today with operating room tomorrow.

We wait until Tom arrives. He drives Vanessa Van almost non-stop from Michigan to Edmonton. It is cold, hard winter driving. He is tired and discouraged when he arrives. He hugs Wendy hard. He is glad she has regained words she lost with the seizure, and that she is brighter.

They go out in the cold searching for a place to live. Tom hates the city. He wants to be somewhere he can see the horizon, hear geese flying overhead and canoe down a river in the spring. But that would mean Wendy would be isolated, not able to drive, waiting for Tom for transportation into the city for her appointments. It is clear now that she desperately needs psychological counselling, more speech therapy, and other services only available in the city.

Tom reluctantly agrees. They find a basement suite on a bus route. It is close to us. This makes us feel good. It is a long, frigid walk to the Glenrose Hospital and to Grant MacEwan's Community Enrichment Program, another place Wendy can find help for her activities of daily living, but Wendy wants to walk. She believes in exercise and knows how to dress for the bitter cold of an Edmonton winter.

Journal Entry: December 23, 1989
Tom and Wendy moved into their own place last night after buying a bed. Tom had flu, but kept going through the filthy weather. It is their first home since the accident. They took over boxes of things that were packed up after the accident from their little house by the lake. They haven't even begun to unpack their wedding presents.

Tom and Wendy come to the family Christmas dinner. Tom is quiet, but Tom is always quiet. Wendy is angry. She can't help with Christmas dinner preparations because she doesn't understand what needs to be done. She doesn't understand when told to get the green placemats or the large dinner forks. In the confusion of our preparations she sulks, engaging someone in conversation, taking them away from the group. Wendy is used to being the centre of attention. She doesn't like it much when her nephews take precedence.

Tom and Wendy go home early. Wendy calls early the next morning wanting to know what we are doing today. Tom has gone off. She doesn't know where. My heart sinks for her. She is so unhappy.

Journal Entry: December 28, 1989

So much has been left undone because Doug, Wendy and Tom were here. It is finally beginning to catch up with me. I am "being available" and not working on anything else.

Wendy calls often. Tom has gone out. Tom is with his friends in St. Albert. Tom isn't there. This is ominous.

Journal Entry: December 30, 1989

Almost the end of the decade. I am 56. I took Doug home on Thursday morning, after he had raged against his back, his inactivity, the fact that his roommates had used his hockey stick, and the fact that he couldn't pick up two pieces of paper. I left him quickly, as I couldn't bear seeing him rage any longer.

Then we took Wendy and Tom to The Faculty Club to have Bill talk about the fact that no one is "co-ordinating" her rehabilitation. We want to help. Wendy doesn't want our help. She wants to co-ordinate her own rehabilitation. I gave her the piece of paper on which I had written the ten things which need attention.

1.   *Medications.*
2.   *Speech therapy.*
3.   *Reading.*
4.   *Writing.*
5.   *Vocational rehabilitation.*
6.   *Psychology.*
7.   *Legal.*
8.   *Computer.*
9.   *Recreation.*
10.   *Doctor appointments.*

Tom, Bill, and I tried to explain that we want to help because things are hard for her, but she doesn't want to know that. When we came home, I lay on my bed trying to come to terms with the fact that I can't make everything right for my children. Not money, or time, or love will fix the problems they have. They must live their own lives. Mothers can only sorrow. I think this is a tough but important step in learning to live again. Accepting that I can't make everything fair and just for my offspring.

Slowly, it becomes apparent that if Wendy needs the city, Tom does not. He stays overnight with old friends who live on an acreage. He says little. Wendy commits to her schedule of speech therapy, psychology and Grant MacEwan's Community Enrichment Program.

The bedroom windows of Tom and Wendy's little apartment face the parking lot. Cars come and go in the dark of the Edmonton winter, blasting headlights into their bedroom, morning and night. They hate it. There is an unsavoury crowd living in the building. It is not satisfactory. They have to move.

Tom goes away more frequently now. Job searches, he says. Wendy says he has a girlfriend. We question Wendy but she hasn't the words to explain. It seems out of the question. We can't believe it. We say nothing.

Tom comes back and they find a house to rent, a little closer to the Glenrose. They move. Perhaps now Tom will not feel so trapped in the city with his front and his back door, his yard, his garage and his basement. But Tom goes away again. He is seldom home. He doesn't show Wendy bus routes, or ways to get around. He doesn't go to appointments with her or take an interest in her psychology or speech therapies. He won't consider psychological counselling for himself. He goes to B.C. for a bear hunt.

Wendy falls back on us for help and for her social life. Again, she says Tom has a girlfriend. She says he got her last summer when she was in Metis, when he was in Valemont working as an outfitter and being in a movie. We don't know how to help.

Chapter 16

The Third Year

Journal Entry: January 10, 1990.

Yesterday Wendy phoned, slurred voiced, words lost, small-girled again. "Her hand.." she tells us, "Tight.. muscles.." She had taken double doses of Dilantin and Tegretol, fearing another seizure. She wanted to be alone. I drove to her apartment. The door was open. There was no response to my bell or knocking. I went in and found her buried under two comforters and pillows, groggy, dizzy, unable to find or form words. Tom has been gone for days. She is sick with worry. She doesn't want to betray him by talking about him, but she says he needs a break. His stomach hurts. He is worried about his job.

Wendy lay in a fug while I folded a little laundry and tidied up the kitchen. I found half-cooked brownies in the oven. She told me that she watched a religious program on TV in the night and phoned them and cried a lot.

She wanted to go to the bank. She had no money. I gave her $20.00 but she was too dizzy to go out. The oven doesn't work. I reported it to the landlord and asked her to keep an eye on Wendy. Then, as I drove home, I railed and ranted to myself that my daughter has these problems and has to deal with them by herself .

Days after that, I go with Bill to Vancouver on a business trip. From there, I go by myself to Point-No-Point on Vancouver Island by the ocean, with my photography equipment, seeking solitude. I shoot the dawn, I shoot waves, cleansing my soul with their repetitive grey-green cresting. I walk. I seek the dark of the rain forest. I try to discover how to photograph the huge trees, larger than lenses. I prepare vegetarian meals. I walk in the rain. I keep a fire burning in the little cabin. I rest. I am quiet. I write.

Journal Entry: February 2, 1990

Home again, 26 months after Wendy's accident, still affected daily by her injuries. "But she looks wonderful," people say, "and she's talking so well too." But behind the scenes her life is so awful.

Yesterday morning Wendy came looking for Dilantin at our house. She had forgotten her own and we had none. She berated me for the things I haven't done, for being a bad mother when the kids were small, and for getting my jollies from being involved with NABIS. She says, "I am your JOB now." I try to clarify what I am doing, to explain, but it is difficult.

She had called the lawyer to tell him that she and Tom are "not going to be married," so if the lawyer knows that, she will get more money and money is what the world is all about. It is all so complex. Trying to capture her confusion, anxiety, bewilderment and perplexity is almost impossible.

Wendy just phoned, saying Tom wants a divorce. This can't be true! I am angry and sad. I think about Tom. I can't bear his pain.. and her pain... and my pain.

She said she wants to come here to live. I said, "But you hate living here, Wendy."

I say. "Plan your day."

"One day at a time."
"One hour at a time."
"Come with me to NABIS tonight. The program is about Caring and Sharing."
later.... It would have been better if she had died.
Better for her, for Tom and for us.
But what is better?
Not long ago, I met a woman whose sixteen-year old son died in hospital after having been in a coma for some months. Someone else told me that her meeting with me had been significant to her. It made her realize that although her son had died, she was free to get on with the rest of her life. She had said, "Mufty is not." Today, I must admit, she is right.

Now in the winter of 1990 we are going on a family holiday. We have saved "bottle money" for 12 years for a special trip and are taking the whole family to Arizona. We buy eleven tickets. Bill, Mufty, Bruce, Michele, Kyle, Kory, Wendy, Tom, Bob and Shelley and Doug.

Journal Entry: Feb. 13, 1990
We still don't know if Tom is coming with us to Arizona.

Journal Entry: February 17, 1990
Tom phoned on his way to the pipeline (having told us that he would not be going with us) to apologize for screwing it all up. But, after talking with Bill, he phoned Wen to say he had changed his mind and that he was coming.

Journal Entry: February 24, 1990 Phoenix, Arizona.
Tom decided at the last moment not to come, so Wendy is suffering terribly. She sits huddled in a corner, staring into nothing, desolate to

understand what is happening in her life. We are all so sad watching her, but she pushes us away if we try to hug or comfort her.

Wendy does not know why Tom has to leave her. One of the great blessings of her situation is that she does not comprehend how handicapped she is. She keeps on trying to do things which she is unable to do. When Tom leaves, she is doubly hurt because he is gone and she doesn't understand. She asks again, "Why did he leave? Hadn't we just got married? Why would he leave?"

Journal Entry: March 15, 1990

It is early morning. I am angry. Angry with Tom. Having been confronted by Wendy with nine phone calls to a phone number in Jasper on her old phone bill, he admitted to having a woman friend, just someone who doesn't know anything about the accident.

The Assured Income for the Severely Handicapped, AISH, has accepted Wendy to their program, but on their records, she is married, is being supported, and is living in an apartment. Supposedly Tom is her guardian. AISH phoned yesterday to finalize the details but discovered that Tom is not supporting Wendy. More confusion, more paperwork, more red tape.

We ask Tom to talk with us. Tom, a man of few words, comes with Wendy. With quivering lip he talks about being weak, about not being able to live with Wendy anymore because he just looks forward to being somewhere else. He says that when she was in the hospital it was easy to know what to do to help. Now he doesn't know what to do. He says that when he is away from Wendy, he has more fun and he knows that is no way to have a marriage, always wanting to be away from her.

We listen. Bill asks if there is another woman. Tom says no. It is just that he cannot live with Wendy. It is a sad hour. We say goodbye and I tell Tom I will always love him and be grateful for all he has done.

Journal Entry: March 23, 1990

Wendy was tested all this week at the Community Enrichment Program. Then she went off to Jasper with Judy Henderson. I bet she's going to go to see Tom's "friend". When Bill asked Tom about his friend, he said there is no romantic involvement. Wendy will probably fix that for him this weekend and go to meet her. Good for Wen.

Apparently, Wendy went past the woman's house with Judy. Who should be there but Tom. Wendy told us this saying, "No hugs, no kisses" when he greeted them. Wendy just doesn't believe the "no romantic involvement" stuff. Apparently Judy was pretty outspoken to Tom. She said it was a very sad day.

Journal Entry: April 4, 1990

I went with Wendy to the university to pick up her computer. It was a bad day. Wendy could hardly control the mouse because of the lack of fine motor co-ordination in her right hand. It was a simple game to demonstrate the use of the mouse. It was very hard for her. She hasn't sufficient concentration to stay at it very long and became frustrated, then silent and inattentive. She made no eye contact with the salesman. So he began to talk to me instead. He's a nice guy and just didn't know how to help Wendy.

Wendy is now beginning to experience and to comprehend her losses. She is depressed. She tries to make dinner for friends and doesn't do very well. She takes them to the museum for what she thinks is a slide show, but it is a reception and opening for wildlife week. She loses her wallet again. When I phone her to ask if I can do anything for her, she says, "Yes, a ride to the bank to get money, please." It isn't until I get to her house that she tells me her wallet is gone again and she doesn't know where. Now she bikes to swim in the mornings and walks to the Glenrose. She is very tired, but still fighting.

Journal Entry: May 17, 1990

Wendy had a seizure Friday night. Bill and I stayed at the hospital with her from 5:30 until 10:30 PM while she had intravenous Dilantin. Her blood Dilantin level was very low.

I learned yesterday that I have cataracts in both eyes, my sight is going downhill fast. I must have two operations in the fall. At NABIS they told me that it is not unusual for family members who live with the effects of brain injuries to develop major health problems. I am just grateful that I can get my sight back!

Journal Entry: May 25, 1990

Now, I learn that I must have a bladder repair and at the same time a hysterectomy. What next! I have been busy trying to find a case co-ordinator to help Wendy when I go into the hospital. I have heard that it is imperative to rest after this operation and I know that it is impossible to rest when responsible for Wendy's business. A case co-ordinator supervises assessment, links Wendy up with whatever she needs, monitors her progress, gives assistance with matters of daily living and does crisis intervention. It is what I have been doing since she came home from Michigan. It is what I have been doing since the accident. Now we need someone else to do it.

Journal Entry: July 5, 1990

My hysterectomy and bladder repair went very well. I felt cared for and it was certainly the easiest operation I have ever had. I am home without energy or drive.

Wendy moves into a little house about seven blocks away from us across from her old Junior High School. The fellow she rents the room from is very willing to learn about her and figure out how best to communicate with her.

Journal Entry: September 9, 1990
Friday last, I went with Wendy to the Examination for Discovery for the man who hit the deer in Wendy's accident. I thought our lawyer, Rob Graesser did a great job, thorough with painstaking details. Chomicki, Mrs. Stelter's lawyer is more aggressive and confrontational. I would be terrified if he had to question me! The next step is to determine, with the lawyers, the exact amount of money the accident has cost us, the damages to Wendy, loss of income, pain and suffering and so forth. This is where they will use all the records we have been keeping. The trial is expected to take two weeks. Probably next June or July. In the meantime, Wendy is doing pretty well in her new house.

Journal Entry: September 20, 1990
My eyes are getting worse but my new glasses are wonderful. I can drive again! We are going to New Orleans at the end of the month. Hurray. I'm ready for a holiday.

Journal Entry: October 12, 1990
Bill and I hadn't got in the door from our holiday in New Orleans when a friend came by to ask how Wendy was. We asked, "What happened to Wendy?" We were told she had a fall on her bike in the ravine just this morning. We phoned her and discovered that she still had a very painful leg, so Bill and I took her to the Emergency at University Hospital. She has a broken fibula and is on crutches. More sad. More pain. More nuisance. I think it is directly related to her drinking and

smoking joints, which Doug reports she did at a Thanksgiving party at her own house.

Journal Entry: October 18, 1990. Sheraton Landmark Hotel, Vancouver.

At the Pacific Coast Brain Injury Conference. Tomorrow, the first day of the conference, is for survivors. Wendy is feeling coerced into coming to this conference, but I hope she will meet some nice people. We went out for dinner last night. Wendy has an interesting coping mechanism when she can't read the menu. She asks the waiter what he would have. He points to the menu as he explains it, which saves her having to read.

My eyesight is so bad that all I can see out the window at night, looking at the vast city below, are little halos of light.

Journal Entry: October 21, 1990

Wendy has had a very good time. She did meet some nice young people, attractive and fun to be with, who valued and understood her. It has been a hugely rewarding experience watching her being relaxed, having fun, and being involved. She now understands the worth of being with other people with head injuries. She is considering going to a similar conference in New Orleans in the middle of November.

I have had fun being with her. I experienced joy watching her use her smile and her genuine interest in others to get to know people. They are charmed. It is my feeling that this conference will be a turning point for her. I enjoyed the plenary sessions, especially those dealing with empowering the survivor.

I have my cataract operations. First one eye, on October 24 and the other on November 7. It is traumatic for me but thrilling to regain brilliant, excellent eyesight!

Chapter 17

Wendy's Case Co-ordination

There are no rehabilitation facilities which suit Wendy's needs, so Wendy creates her own group. What a spirited woman! I am so proud of her. The group agrees to meet at the Glenrose Hospital with her to discuss her rehabilitation. The group includes me, a counsellor, a speech therapist, a psychologist, Bill, and Wendy as chair.

1st CASE CO-ORDINATION MEETING
October 16, 1990

Wendy co-ordinates. We discuss her recreation, flute lessons, money, reading lessons, computer, community enrichment program, speech therapy, psychology and groups. Wendy decides that she will make regular appointments for speech therapy, community enrichment program and help with calendar management. She will have regular visits with the psychologist to work on her self-concept, ego identity, realistic hopefulness, problem solving, memory management and anger management.

Finally there is some co-ordination of all the components of

Wendy's rehabilitation. We decide to meet in six weeks. Fantastic Wendy, the one with the brain injury has taken charge. Way to go, Wendy, way to go! Just like when she was five and organizing her brothers.

Journal Entry: November 13, 1990
Wendy is being picked up by a friend who works for Delta Air Lines. She will put Wendy on a flight to New Orleans where she will attend the American Brain Injury Conference. I am frightened that she will lose her ticket, her money, her book which tells where she is going, or forget to take her Dilantin. I worry that she will have a drink which will cause another seizure. I clamp my worries to myself. The important thing is that she is going. By herself!

Wendy comes back saying that it wasn't as good as the conference in Vancouver. She learns that she doesn't leave her difficulties behind, she doesn't speak better or understand more in New Orleans. Wendy and three friends from the Pacific Coast Brain Injury Conference in Vancouver participated in a play at the New Orleans conference. As well, they created an important document called "What Survivors of Brain Injury Want You to Know."

What Survivors of Brain Injury Want You to Know

The members of the New Orleans LHIF Peer Support Group met and discussed what they would like medical and rehabilitation professionals to know when they are communicating or working with someone who has had a brain injury. Suggestions and comments were made in several areas, including how to treat and talk to the person who has survived a brain injury and how to understand what it feels like to have had life changed by the injury.

Survivors of brain injury would like you to know the following:

1. We would like to be treated as you would want someone to treat you and someone you loved.

2. We would like to be treated with dignity and respect even though we might have problems and you might think we are being difficult sometimes.

3. Don't treat us as if we're misfits. We're not stupid.

4. Make sure you're giving us good advice and telling us the right way to do something.

5. Say, "I don't know" when you don't know the answer to our questions. It might be frustrating to us for you to say that, but it's better than telling us something that might not be true.

6. Tell us when improvement will take a long time.

7. Realize how much courage it takes to keep going after a brain injury.

8. Get to know us as a person and get to know the best way to communicate with us.

9. Help us find out what will motivate us. Learn what keeps us from giving up or giving in.

10. We value people who give us encouragement. Encourage us to be the best we can be.

11. Recognize that there are things we can do well.

12. Positive feedback is beneficial to us, but don't patronize us or do it so much that it loses its value.

13. Ask us what helps.

14. Give us a chance and let us take risks sometimes.

15. Tell us you'll do your best to help us get to our best level.

16. Tell us what "normal" means to you.

17. Try to understand what it feels like to have our lives

changed so much by brain injury. Try to think what it's like to "walk in our shoes".

18. Realize that we feel lonely and isolated sometimes.

19. Realize that it might be difficult for our old friends to "Handle" the injury and that it might be hard for us to make new friends.

20. Don't say, "Everybody has trouble remembering or everybody does something like that sometimes," unless you show us you understand that our problems are important and probably not the same as the "usual" problems someone has when they haven't had a brain injury.

While Wendy is away, Bob visits from Whitehorse. We have a family conference to update everyone on Wendy's progress. My eyes improve. I can see well at a distance. I am elected president of NABIS.

Journal Entry: December 1, 1990

Wendy was very aware of the third anniversary of her accident. We spent the morning in the U. of A. Emergency department because she had a fever and shortness of breath. Erythromycin prescribed.

AISH have not known about Wendy's Canada Disability Pension payments. I learned on Monday that Wendy has been overpaid in the amount of $4,000. Now her income will be about $600 a month instead of $1,200. Bill and I will augment her income which will be a major adjustment for us. More problems!

Journal Entry: December 6, 1990

Today I needed to write a letter to the Caucus Committee of the Government of Alberta about the many needs of people with brain injuries. The Executive Director of NABIS and I will be meeting with them in the near future. It is difficult to get a hearing so it is important to spend the time planning and organizing what we will say.

I spent yesterday at a government stakeholders meeting about brain injury services. Departments are realizing that individuals with brain injuries are falling between the cracks of service so have set up fact finding meetings involving people affected by brain injury. I am there as a family member.

I must phone Disabled Adult Transportation System, DATS, who seem unable to pick up Wendy when she thinks they should. When I spoke with them before, I asked what information they have about her in their computer. Did they know that she had difficulty in understanding the spoken word over the telephone? Did they have it marked on her file that when making appointments with her, times must be double checked? What do they have beside her name?

They said, "Mentally Retarded." Inside I raged. I said, in as controlled a voice as I could, "That is incorrect. She is not mentally retarded. She has had a brain injury. Would you please mark her file somehow so those who were making the appointments for her pick-ups would know that."

Their answer was that they don't have a computer classification for people with brain injuries, just mentally retarded. I asked to speak to the manager. I retold the problem. I asked her if there was some way they could mark Wendy's file that she has communication difficulties and they need to double check times for her. The manager was very sorry, but they are unable to do that. They do not have a classification for "people like Wendy."

2nd CASE CO-ORDINATION MEETING
Dec. 2, 1990

We have another case co-ordination meeting to plan for the next six weeks. Bill and I are there again with the same professionals and two new people, one a computer assistant, the other a recreation therapist. Many of the tasks identified at the last meeting have been done. Much has gone by the wayside. Wendy will check with her high school music teacher about the possibility of joining the Cosmopolitan Music Band. Psychology counselling will continue only when Wendy wants it. Wendy will work on reading. I am to buy a hand-held recorder with batteries for this purpose. We are on track together again. Next meeting in six weeks.

Journal Entry: January 23, 1991

Wendy cancelled her case co-ordination meeting for Thursday because she didn't think we needed one. It made me a little uneasy, but she was right. We are on track with everything.

Three years, two months since the accident and there are still too many loose ends in the court case to set a court date. I keep phoning Rob to give him information to try to push it along. The advice we got at the beginning was to phone the lawyer regularly to maintain the momentum. That, as well as everything else there is to do for Wendy! I have an appointment with Rob next week.

Journal Entry: January 30, 1991

Wendy just phoned to ask me to drive her to the university. DATS doesn't allow for any last-minute trips. Appointments must be made two days in advance. I asked her if she could possibly get there on her own and she said she could. She is lonely and down this morning. I said I needed rest and she said OK. She would take the bus. I phoned her back to ask her why she didn't get DATS regularly. She said, "How would you like to take DATS? People ask questions? What's wrong with you? How do you feel this morning?"

"Oh, is that the problem, Wendy?" I said. "Have people ever asked you those questions?" "I'll talk to you another time." she said and hung up.

Journal Entry: February 8, 1991

Wendy invited people to dinner at our house Wednesday night, two friends from the recreation department at the university. What super people! Wendy has permission to audit any lecture she wants at any time. It helps her to feel the way she was before the accident, attending lectures as she used to do. It was a special evening.
But the bad news is more trouble with DATS!

3rd CASE CO-ORDINATION MEETING
Feb. 14, 1991

We sit around the same room with the same people reviewing what has happened since the last meeting. It is becoming apparent how difficult it is to get everything done with Wendy impulsively going off in other directions. She has now joined a kayaking club. The computer work isn't getting done. The recreation therapist will look into ski clubs. Wendy is going to Cosmopolitan Music Band in their Thursday night group. There are letters to write for her: to her lawyer and DATS. Psychology should begin again so we must contact AISH. Not much assured about this!
Wendy has heard about a recreation forum for people with disabilities and wants to talk on the importance of recreation for people with brain injuries. Will I help? Generally things are on track. Wendy will call the next meeting when she feels the need.

Journal Entry: February 25, 1991 2:25 am
Bill and I are very sad. We learned that Wendy had a seizure last Friday

night. We didn't see her until Saturday morning. She had lost her registration slip for the extension course in Sexuality of Women, so Bill and I drove her around the university for two hours, trying to find it. She has slipped a lot in comprehension and speech, making her slow of thought and really dozy. As well, she fell skiing and has hurt her leg again. She is angry with herself again. She says she wants to shoot herself.

She came for dinner last night and is quite lost about what to do next. She doesn't want to spend any more time in hospitals. She has lost a lot of ground because she's been smoking marijuana which, like alcohol, triggers the seizures. Then she feels guilty and we are angry, impatient and terribly sad.

Journal Entry: March 1, 1991

Wendy's lawyer told me yesterday that the court case will take three weeks. A date of March 30, 1992 has been set. I couldn't believe it was thirteen months away! He explained that he alone will have 23 witnesses. I was desolate after the call. Thirteen months! That means Wendy will be financially dependent on us for at least thirteen more months! Poor darling! No wonder she is angry.

Journal Entry: March 20, 1991

Wendy came by at 7.30 AM, as she wanted help writing a letter. Then again before supper, wanting to talk to Bill. We had supper together and then I drove her to a Toastmasters group she just joined. She keeps on joining groups and classes, hoping that they will be the answer to her problems.

Journal Entry: March 24, 1991. Sunday night

My dear friend Elaine, who is home at last, says I spend a lot of my time being sad. Perhaps she is right. I must watch myself. I was

sorrowful this evening when Wendy came over and was very glum.
Finally, she blurted out that she will be divorced as of May 21.
Elaine is right. I am sad tonight, and almost every night. Sad for what
might have been without Wendy's accident. How it goes on and on. I
feel drained and empty.

4th CASE CO-ORDINATION MEETING
April 18, 1991

We have another meeting with a new member, a teacher working with adolescents in the hospital. Wendy has been volunteering at the hospital helping with teens in her reading program. They see themselves as helping her and Wendy sees herself as helping them.

The computer is still a problem. We need a referral to the Assistive Devices Clinic at the Glenrose. Wendy wants to go to an outdoor program at Camrose College. I will find details. Doctor appointments must be made. We are searching for a teacher-aide for continued attention to Wendy's reading. They do not return my calls.

Journal Entry: April 18, 1991

Bill and I went to Bruce's hockey game last night. The game ended
abruptly when one of the players hit his head on the ice and had a
seizure. An ambulance came and took him away. I just stood there
crying.

The teacher at the Glenrose invites Wendy to her farm. Wendy meets,
and likes, Jimmy, a jockey, who is incredibly good with horses. They see
one another often.

Wendy moves into an apartment by herself close to the university.

Journal Entry: June 2, 1991

I went to lunch with Wendy at the farm where her new boyfriend lives. He seems to be a nice man and if he makes Wendy happy, I am happy for Wendy.

Journal Entry: June 8, 1991

Bill's life has fallen apart at work. We were alone this morning for the first time, intending to talk about it, but when I went to where he was reading the paper, I found Wendy there, with another crisis. Her apartment is flooded. Badly. Jimmy brought her here. And all I can feel in my exhaustion is resentment. What to do with resentment? How I hate myself for feeling this way. Oh, dear!

5th CASE CO-ORDINATION MEETING
June 26, 1991

Six people involved now. Wendy, speech therapist, teacher, psychologist, Bill, and me. The computer problem is ongoing. We will check the Volunteer Action Centre for a volunteer. Assistive Devices people can't see Wendy until the fall! The psychologist will try to find someone to continue the reading tutoring. She will work out a game plan for Wendy. She will make time to have some longer appointments to deal with legitimate day-to-day concerns. The Glenrose is exploring the possibilities of vocational assessment and training. Next meeting, July 30.

Wendy is a little more independent now. She is involved with Jimmy during this time. It is not a smooth relationship but she is out of doors, being with friends and having a boyfriend. She goes on a trail ride with him during the summer which is a disaster. There is rain every day and a bad scene with a truck getting stuck on a hill in a sea of mud, with all the horses tied into the truck. It was a frightening episode and from what I can understand, Wendy was very upset and aggressive. She hit Jimmy. This ends the relationship. Wendy tells us she hit Tom and Doug since the accident. Controlling aggression is an ongoing problem for many people with brain injuries. Wendy is no exception.

6th CASE CO-ORDINATION MEETING
July 30, 1991

We meet again in the small, square room with the square table on the fourth floor of the Glenrose Hospital. Wendy still chairs the meetings. The same people are there, plus two new people from Social Work.

Bill and Wendy have investigated software alternatives for her computer. Wendy still needs a person who knows Apple Computers to assist her in using the program. Her tutor reports that Prospects Literacy will find a volunteer teacher for the fall. The University of Alberta Services for Students with Disabilities is involved. It is important to let both services know what the other is being asked.

Wendy needs a medical referral for special library resources. Wendy continues to work towards readiness for driving assessment. Wendy and the psychologist try two-hour sessions to work on skill building and they will continue two-hour appointments once a week in September.

The Grant MacEwan representative knows of a program, starting at the Glenrose, called DECSA, that gives opportunity for work experience. He will investigate. The speech therapist reports there is another out-patient group working on memory improvement starting again in the fall. Wendy will join. Next meeting, Oct 1.

There are no entries in my journals about Wendy for many months. The first is in September, when she and I go to Calgary to check out the Reading Foundation. All this time, Wendy lives in her basement apartment alone. It feels far away from us. She is lonely. She forgets to buy food for her meals and forgets to eat. Especially supper. I realize she doesn't think about eating anything in her cupboard unless she actually opens the door and sees something. When she goes shopping for herself she buys what she sees. Making a list and planning for what she will need in the week ahead doesn't work. I make up a two-week menu for her with a list of what she might want to keep in her cupboards. She forgets the list.

7th CASE CO-ORDINATION MEETING
OCTOBER 1, 1991

Wendy is eligible for a personal support worker through AISH. We need to define specifically what it is that Wendy needs so that we can get a letter from the doctor verifying her need. We can get approval from AISH for the expense of this person. Wendy has a new AISH worker who is unfamiliar with her case. He has just acquired a new caseload and is having difficulty getting to know all his clients. However I will re-submit a request for a personal support worker. That person needs expertise in Apple computers and reading and writing skills. Wendy will work with her present computer for the time being.

Recreation Update: The application for the Rick Hansen Centre has been submitted. The focus will be fitness oriented. No recreation like basketball teams has been found yet. Prospects Literacy has not yet found anyone to assist Wendy through the University system.

Bill has found a new clinic teaching reading in Calgary.

Wendy has an appointment for October 3 for an assessment and recommendations. It will cost $250. If successful, they offer four hours per day for a one month period. We will know the results immediately after the test. Psychology focus is on anger management. Wendy attends a Volunteer Development Group which is going well. The memory group is fairly satisfactory. She has discontinued the Problem Solving Group as it is not meeting her needs. Wendy will attend the Pacific Coast Brain Injury Symposium in October in Vancouver. There is a Pre-Conference workshop on Vocational Evaluation which is timely. Next meeting, when Wendy says.

Chapter 18

The Reading Foundation

It is a cold, blustery fall day. Wendy and I speed with the early morning traffic to take the exit ramp off the south-bound Blackfoot trail in Calgary. We travel east to a large, square, yellow brick building which is the home of the Reading Foundation. Wendy likes it because it is away from the downtown core.

We find the north door open in the pre-dawn light. We walk along a grey corridor and up the grey, sealed stairwell to the second floor where, at the end of the corridor through a plain brown door, we reach our destination.

The smiling receptionist is expecting us and makes us feel at home. The chairs around the yellow-walled waiting room are filled with other mothers and their children. The mothers are in their twenties and thirties; the children, between seven and late teens. We are out of place here, my being fifty-seven and Wendy thirty-one, but this is unimportant. We have an appointment with Steven Truch, director of the foundation.

He will test Wendy this morning. Reading tests and writing tests. She is excited with the attention, childlike in her determination to do well, but she hates needing to have her mother there, hates being dependent.

We have done this before. We have been to the Reading and Language Centre in the Faculty of Education at the University of Alberta. They worked with Wendy on tutoring sessions for ten weeks. In an eleven-page report, dated April 1991, they say that Wendy needs more. More intensive and regular literacy learning opportunities, possibly a tutor, a couple of times a week. But no one knows how to find the right tutor.

Before that, in June of 1989 we went to the Sylvan Learning Centre in Edmonton for an interview. They proposed working with Wendy for twenty-minute sessions, two or three times a day. This was not very practical.

We also went to St. Anthony's Teacher Centre to find a teacher. They suggested the head of language arts at the Catholic School Board. They recommended music therapy at the Charles Camsell Hospital. They also suggested the music supervisor of the Catholic School Board. We have followed all these leads and many more. We are nowhere.

Back at the Reading Foundation, we are offered coffee or juice and shortly a greying, smiling man approaches us and introduces himself as Steve Truch. We introduce ourselves and he is wonderfully welcoming. He looks carefully at us both, and directs what he says at Wendy. This is immediately reassuring. We have met so many people who talk to "the Mum," as though Wendy is invisible.

He shows us around the offices where we see many brightly-lit, comfortable rooms each with a teacher and student working, usually around a table with large cards of pictures and letters. There are blackboards in each room, alphabets, photographs and books. It is relatively quiet, with gentle, subdued talking and murmuring as we move from room to room. The children look happy and engaged, the teachers interested and involved.

Steve asks me to wait as it will take some time to do Wendy's initial testing. I go outside for a walk in the cold, sunny day. I love the grey Chinook arches over the semi-circle of cobalt blue over the distant mountains in the southwest sky. They mean that warm winds will blow from the west all day. I walk along the crest on the east side of the Bow River, silently beseeching the gods and goddesses to intervene and make this the right place for Wendy, praying that Steve will find the Reading Foundation and their methods of teaching one-on-one will indeed help Wendy re-learn reading. The warm wind is a benediction on my face. I go back to the waiting room, where a new set of mothers and children wait.

At length, Wendy and Steve come out. Wendy's eyes have lost their light. Steve asks us to come into a room so that he can tell us the results of the tests. We sit while he gathers papers.

He begins. There are tears in his eyes. He says, "Wendy's scores are very low. She is reading at a grade one level and less."

I look at Wendy and she too, has tears in her eyes. She is like a little girl, ashamed to have her test results so low as though she has not done her homework, or has not worked quite hard enough. As though it is her fault. Oh, Wendy dear!

But this is the bad news. The good news is that Steve is confident they can help. He explains. Their methods relate to the pre-phonics problems of phonemes or sounds in spoken words. Wendy is diagnosed as missing these phonemes which means she is unable to have the tools to decode a word. She is unable to comprehend what is said or written. He is certain that they can help Wendy. It will be tough, especially because of her very short concentration span. If she agrees, they will work for four hours each morning, each hour with a new teacher. Pre-phonemic processing.

Steve learned this method at the Lindamood Bell Processing Clinic at San Luis Obispo, near San Francisco. He has brought it back to Calgary and has started this Reading Foundation. He serves children failing in the school system, where he worked as a psychologist for many years. He became frustrated because, no matter what the teachers did, they were simply not teaching the children to read. He brought this method to Calgary, trained staff, and is having phenomenal success.

Steve introduces us to another young woman who also sustained a brain injury. She is full of the joys of relearning to read. She has jumped many grades in her two years at the Foundation. Wendy chats with her and is filled with hope. Steve takes me aside and tells me quietly that he has never tested anyone with such low scores. But he is sure they can help.

We drive back to Edmonton, talking all the way about whether or not Wendy should try it. I think it will be fabulous. I am impressed with the no-claim attitude of Steve but with his controlled excitement about teaching Wendy the basic tools for speech and reading. I could tell that he felt Wendy had massive potential, especially when he learned of her ability to read a city map to get us to the clinic. He was even more thrilled to learn that she can read music, and finds that significant.

Wendy is pleased, but unsure. She doesn't understand the technical material, but Bill and I are very enthusiastic. Her always being game for learning sways her.

We need money. I write to Aunty Kit. She is ninety-one now and told us that if Wendy ever needed anything, she would be glad to pay for it, so we ask again.

Aunty Kit phones the day she gets the letter. "I got your letter, darling, and of course I will help. Whatever amount you need for Wendy. Just tell me how much and how you want me to pay and I will send her a cheque."

I thank her profusely and hang up the phone, full of relief. My gratitude is profound. All through this ordeal we have been given what we needed when we needed it. It never ceases to surprise me. I have an enormous faith that we will not be asked to do any more than we are capable of.

REPORT OF ASSESSMENT, READING FOUNDATION.
October 1991

Summary and Recommendations: Wendy is an adult whose life has been traumatically affected by an automobile accident. Prior to the accident, she had completed a Bachelor's degree from the University of Alberta in Recreation. While some basic language processes have recovered since the accident, the literacy processes have not significantly advanced.

In Wendy's case, both decoding and comprehension are affected to a severe degree.

In the case of decoding/encoding, disrupted phonemic procession at the sub-lexical level of speech is responsible.

In the case of comprehension, the link between visual imagery procession and language and thought procession is disturbed.

Wendy is therefore a candidate for both therapies offered at the Reading Foundation. This therapy begins at the phonemic level of speech and thinking and proceeds in small steps of success from there. Overlap to reading and spelling occurs once the foundation is solidly established.

In the case of comprehension, therapy begins at a very basic level of visual processing, links into language and proceeds to written and oral language only when the foundation is established. Therapy is very intense. Ideally, we see students four hours daily, five days a week. for four consecutive weeks for each therapy. Therapy is administered by trained clinicians under closely supervised conditions in order to maximize gains. Post-testing is done at the end of 80 hours in order to measure gains and determine future needs.

In Wendy's situation, it is impossible to give a reasonable estimate of how much therapy is required. This does become more apparent once she enters the program and is something that is carefully monitored.

I would be pleased to answer any question or concerns regarding this therapy, especially with reference to Wendy's needs.

Steve Truch, Ph.D. Consulting Psychologist

Late in October, Wendy moves to Calgary to attend the Reading Foundation. She travels to Calgary on Sunday night by bus and stays with a young couple who have registered their home with the Reading Foundation to take in students. We arrange a taxi to pick her up and return her to the house after lunch each day. Transportation for disabled persons is much more satisfactory in Calgary than in Edmonton.

She keeps her apartment in Edmonton so that she can come home on weekends to live in her own place with her own things.

Journal Entry: Monday, November 4, 1991
I have been worrying about Wendy since early morning. She was quite angry with me all weekend and I wonder if the strain of the Reading Foundation is getting to her. I hope she can see it through. How can I help from Edmonton? Once again I am trying to evaluate how Wendy is from afar.

Journal Entry: November 26, 1991

Today is four days before the fourth anniversary date of Wendy's accident. It is driving her nuts. The anniversary date is a really hard day for all survivors.

I spent from ten to one with Wendy today, preparing her to go back to Calgary for the next few days. She felt she had "lost it" last Friday at the Reading Foundation and that the one-on-one is too intense for her. I think so too. So Bill, Doug, Wendy and I have been going over and over and over what to do next. Whether or not she should go back, wondering if it would be too much for her. Finally it was decided that she would go back for Tuesday, Wednesday and Thursday. Bill will go down on Wednesday night, see Steve Truch and talk about what to do next.

Should Wendy move to Calgary?

Journal Entry: December 6, 1991

Another sad day for me with Wendy. We went to the lawyer's office at ten, by which time I was already exhausted with her. She was so angry that she took a cab downtown and I drove the car to the very same location. She is in so much mental pain that I can hardly bear to be with her any more. I feel like Tom. I'd better get out before I do her some damage.

Let me record here. The Damages Claim Summary is for a huge sum of money. There is not enough money for all this pain and suffering. How could this be easier?

My friend Elaine listens to my complaints about how difficult it is to live with Wendy. She says that she thinks I am being too defensive, trying to explain why things have happened. She suggests I go with Wendy's feelings, validate the way she feels. If Wendy says, "Why did Tom leave?", I could say, "Wendy, you must be feeling very lonely." If Wendy says, "Mum, you never do anything to help me". I could reply, "Wendy, are you feeling badly that you don't have enough help?" I try this technique and it works well. Wendy just melts at being understood. We avoid a fight, and my recognizing how she feels validates and acknowledges her.

Journal Entry: December 8, 1991
I was so sad, so impossibly sad about Wendy's cooking, about her perseverance, her hair, her indecision, her anger and her sarcastic remarks about my just doing what I want for myself, that I was almost immobilized. I realized I could use some help! So while I was working at NABIS I asked the support worker for counselling. The outcome was her suggestion that I back off, give myself a break. Take TIME OFF. That felt miraculously right. So that is what I have done. Phoned Wendy and told her that I am taking time out. She thinks it a great idea and I feel massive relief.

Journal Entry: December 15, 1991
The pressure has been off re: Wendy. In speaking with her social worker at the Glenrose, he said he was glad I have taken a break. He suggested that I was "over involved" and it made all things possible for Wendy. If instead, Bill and I withdraw some of our support, she will have to face the fact that she cannot have as many options as she thinks she has and she must settle down, especially related to the anger management. We all have to pull together to do this.

Journal Entry: December 23, 1991
A Home Care nurse is coming here at 9 to talk to me and Bill about the "Cost of Future Care" assessment she must do for Wendy for the legal case. She has interviewed Wendy and now will interview us.

Journal Entry: January 14, 1992
I have just read the document from the Home Care nurse, telling of

Wendy's future needs. It tells of her loneliness and vulnerability.

Bill and I went to the AISH appeal board on Monday to appeal their decision not to support the Reading Foundation. We were well prepared and after an hour of educating the board members, we won!

Wendy is home this weekend for an appointment with the neurosurgeon who first admitted her on Nov. 30 in 1987. He hasn't seen her since. However the lawyers must ask him to be a witness, so he has said he is unable to appear for her unless he examines her again. This is happening with the neurosurgeon, the psychologists, the speech therapists, her physician, and others. It is very annoying for Wendy, who has finally found a place to work on her reading and now must interrupt it to come back to Edmonton to have all these appointments and evaluations. Their focus is on what she cannot do. The results are extremely negative, instead of focusing, as we do, on the positive of what she can do.

This legal business is difficult but necessary when trying to get what is just for the injured party.

Journal Entry: February 15, 1992

Wendy is home for the weekend, unhappy with her apartment. I went with her to Dr. Low's yesterday for a medical update before court. She hates having her mother come to her doctor appointments, but she is beginning to realize that it helps everybody, even her.

Journal Entry: February 25, 1992

Wendy just phoned (from Calgary) and asked me to help her write a book about her last four years. I said I would be honoured. I said that nothing would make me prouder than to write a book with her.

Chapter 19
The Trial

Journal Entry: March 21, 1992
Now Wendy is home and finished with the Reading Foundation. The
lawyer for the woman who hit the deer in Wendy's accident has made
a pitiful offer to Wendy's lawyer. We refused it. We now know that
Jasper Automotives, the employers of Eigaard and Van Doorn, has less
than one million dollars of insurance so Rob Graesser has alerted
Wendy's insurance policy people that there might be a claim on them.
The decisions of the next month will make a major difference in
Wendy's life, and in ours.

Early in Wendy's recovery, we asked a lawyer friend of ours to
recommend a lawyer for us to hire. He did some research and
recommended Rob Graesser. We met with Rob, liked him immediately
and engaged him to handle the case. Early on he told us, "My tools are
information. Keep all the records you can about Wendy. Keep a journal.
Keep track of all she does and when she does it. A chronology is
invaluable in preparation for the trial. As well, keep bills and careful
records of all your expenses. Record every cost that you would not
have had to spend if there had been no accident. Information is the base

of the case, so keep accurate information."

So I have kept important dates in my journal, kept files, made notes, kept Wendy's notes to us, kept bills, kept copies of assessments and evaluations. I have given all of this to Rob. He says the case is easier because I have done this so well.

Journal Entry: March 26, 1992

It is as though time has slowed into slow motion. So much of importance might happen in the next few days that we wait, wondering if every phone call might be a proposed settlement, preparing at the same time for three weeks in court.

Wendy phoned last night and told us she got a job at a YMCA camp as a volunteer for the first session in the summer and possibly as paid staff after that. She starts May 1. She was so excited when she told us. It was fabulous to hear her. Bill and I clung to each other after the phone call, both weeping with excitement and wonder at her remarkable abilities!

Journal Entry: March 29, 1992. Sunday. Eve of Wendy's trial.

Housework calms me. Making beds, doing laundry, cooking, ironing or baking keeps me going.

My concentration is very poor. Bill confided last night that his eye has "gone down" and says it is because of the stress. He loses the colour and sight in his eyes with intense stress. It is a type of migraine. He refers to it by saying "my eye has gone down."

March 30, 1992. The trial begins at 10 am at the Law Court Building, 5th floor, Room 511. "Mathewson and Kehoe vs. Stelter and Eigaard and Van Doorn," it says on the door.

There are three long benches the width of the court room. There is a seat for the judge above all, a court reporter ready with her stenograph typewriter, a jury box to the left of two large tables clustered about by lawyers in long, flowing black robes. They rifle through documents.

At ten to ten, Rob Graesser comes quietly into the courtroom and asks us out into the hall to talk with him. He tells us that Mrs. Stelter, the woman who hit the deer and then smashed into Wendy's car, wants to settle out of court. She admits her liability and will settle for the amount requested of her.

We are jubilant. We agree. We are now out of the woods financially in that Wendy will have adequate funds to live on for the rest of her life in the form of a structured settlement. The court adjourns for the day.

The trial must proceed to try to and collect more money from Eigaard and Van Doorn, and to determine Tom's liability, if any.

There is no offer of settlement from Mr. McGinnis, the lawyer for Eigaard and Van Doorn, the men who originally hit the deer, left it on the highway for at least five minutes, didn't put out flares or even put their hazard lights on or try to warn anyone of the danger or move themselves off the highway, so the trial will proceed. Wendy's lawyers must refocus the case against only Eigaard and Van Doorn. Rob says now he is hoping to secure money that will mean Wendy has some "quality of life."

It is determined that it shall be a jury trial. Surprised, we learn that a jury, in Canada, is made up of six people. Five men and one woman have been chosen.

The following day we return. We sit in the front row prepared for a long sit, as three weeks of court time have been assigned to this trial. Rob assures us that we will probably not need all that time. This morning there is me and Bill, Wendy, Tom, Bruce, my friend Nims, from Vancouver Island and Aunty Anne.

The jurors file in. The lawyers bustle. The court reporter is poised over her stenograph. All stand. Judge Andrekson comes in and takes his place. He looks about the courtroom. He asks the lawyers to come forward and speaks quietly to them. Bill and I are asked to leave the room. Because we will be witnesses later on in the week, we must be excluded from hearing testimony until after we have been on the stand. Wendy stays.

Rob gives his opening address. Tom is the first witness. He has come from Valemont, BC. He sits beside Wendy, waiting.

We are exhausted from the tension but have a session at Rob Graesser's house this evening to be told what kinds of questions to expect tomorrow. We go home.

We are told that Tom is a totally credible witness. He is clear and concise. He is clean-cut, well spoken, and an attractive young man. He obviously has the sympathy of the jurors. He is cross-examined.

Bill and I are next.

In the morning I am called to the witness box. I am surprised at how high it feels, sitting, at eye level with the jurors, looking down on the lawyers and the three, long rows of spectators. The judge is behind me and to my left, the jurors to my right.

Rob asks me many questions. What was Wendy like before her accident? What she was like as a little girl? As a teenager? As a young woman? I answer clearly and positively. It is not difficult for me to tell these people about my terrific daughter. I think she is a remarkable, unique young woman. It is my job to tell the court these things. The questioning takes all morning and all afternoon. Finally, Rob gives me a letter which Wendy wrote to me from the camp Tom and Wendy were at for the summer before the accident. It is dated just weeks before the accident. It is eight pages long. It is a dream of a letter responding to a book I had sent her called *Mothers and Daughters*. She tells me her thoughts, and of her plans for her master's degree. She tells of adventures of her summer, of meeting a bear on the trail, of cooking in the cook house. She tells of her decision to live with Tom. It is a personal letter, difficult for me to read. I gave it to Rob three years earlier and had forgotten its contents. It is very dear to me. Wendy shares her honesty throughout. I have a little trouble reading the letter, but I manage.

Cross examination of me the next morning is courteous and mild. It is done quickly. Then it is time for Bill to take the stand. Now, I am allowed to be present.

They ask him similar questions. The focus for his questioning is Wendy's working life. Her history, the ability she had with her business, "Uneek Experience." Bill's mouth becomes straighter and straighter. Rob asks another question. Bill starts to cry. He is unable to answer. Judge Andrekson quickly calls a recess and we all walk out to the waiting room. Rob goes with Bill. They walk over to the windows, Rob's hand on Bill's shoulder. Bill breathes deeply, listens quietly to Rob and is soon ready to go on again. He finishes, is cross-examined gently and the first week is over.

The following week begins with testimony from the Dean of the Department of Recreation at the University of Alberta. Wendy met with him the week before her accident to discuss her application for a master's program in Australia. He speaks about what an excellent candidate she would have made. What a natural fit she was as a Recreation Administrator. Then Gerry Taunton, the expert on the cost of future care, loss of future income and costs to the family, gives his testimony.

I sit listening to these people give evidence on Wendy's behalf. I am seeing pictures. Of course there are no cameras allowed in the court room, but I am at a loss to do something with the nervous energy of listening to all the witnesses. I am compelled to sketch the people of the court because I feel I must capture it. I draw the jurors, the judge, the court stenographer, the lawyers. The latter are the hardest as they are moving about all the time. I draw whoever is in the witness box. I stuff the drawings out of sight in my folder and watch Wendy's trial unfold.

Bill sits through all the technical matters. When I can't stand the tension any more, I go home and do mindless tasks about the house. I make beds, do laundry, make meals. We rent movies at the video store, inane movies to pass the evenings.

Wendy is socializing and is being looked after by Bruce, who has taken time off work to be there. Bill does the food shopping. We put one foot in front of the other, not sleeping well, anxious, tense, hearing things we don't want to hear. We don't want to hear that she will never work again, that she will never be able to live independently, that she will need assistance for the rest of her life.

Mrs. Stelter testifies. Hearing her tell of crashing into Wendy's car is awful. She says when her car came to a stop, she ran over to look into Wendy's car and saw both Wendy and Tom unconscious. I cringe when I imagine the scene. She tells of a car stopping, going the other way. The man had a telephone in his car and reported the accident.

Margaret Brackstone , psychologist, asks that Bill and I not be present for her testimony. She will tell of Wendy's very personal losses, her fears, her ways of coping, successfully and unsuccessfully. We agree, as we do not want to hear this part. We need to believe in Wendy's ongoing improvement. We are sure Margaret will say that we deny the seriousness of Wendy's handicap, that we are not realistic about her ability to recover. Denial is useful for us. We leave.

A neuropsychologist testifies in an incredibly damaging report which says Wendy will never recover, and will have major deficits for the rest of her life. Again, we do not attend. We need to believe that she will regain some of these abilities. Not yet, we say. "YET" is our word. Yet leaves the door open for later. We do not believe in "NEVER", but the court hears the experts say that Wendy will never recover some of her skills.

We are half way through the second week. Now the trial bogs down with technical data. Engineers with sterling, flawless qualifications give evidence about skid marks, how far bright lights on a car project ahead, how far do "dims" project, how long it takes to see an object the size and colour of a deer lying on a road, how long it takes to hit the brakes; when you are twenty, thirty-five, fifty-five? How much of an angle will the car veer if hit on one side or the other? Facts, statistics, data on which to build a case.

Finally, our last witness. Wendy.

I feel so proud, seeing her take the stand. She has come so far. She stands unselfconsciously and looks at the judge, the jury and the lawyer. She is great. She answers the questions well. She asks Rob to repeat them if she doesn't understand them, which happens quite often. She looks at the jurors when she tells her hesitating answers, searching for words that she knows. They cannot help but love her.

Among other questions Rob asks, "Wendy, how do you feel about seeing a psychologist?" She answers slowly, "Well, she's a psychologist, isn't she? How would you like to have to see a psychologist?"

Right on, Wendy. Right on!

The jurors laugh, the lawyers laugh, and the judge laughs too.

The cross-examination is brief and not difficult. Wendy is exhausted when it is over. During her questioning, it becomes evident how much her speech is affected. It is also really clear that she has difficulty understanding the words spoken to her. Rob tells the court that his evidence is finished. Wendy goes home to her own apartment and sleeps the clock around. We too are exhausted watching and willing things to go well for her.

On Friday of the second week there is a new twist. Lawyers for the defence file an application for a non-suit by Lionel Eigaard. The jury is dismissed for the day, the judge and counsel meet to discuss precedents. Court is adjourned until the defence lawyer returns and brings matters to the judge. McGinnis files for a mistrial. We might have to reschedule and go over all this business again!

　　We wait. Thank goodness Eva Stelter has settled.

Journal Entry: April 3, 1992

It was said in court that Bill and I deny the seriousness of the catastrophe. That Wendy will never work in the competitive market place. That she is unable to balance her bank account. That she is vulnerable. That she has uncontrollable mood swings. That she has poor judgment. That travelling with her is like travelling with a small child. That she says things which are unacceptable. That she must have a trustee, and that there will be no appreciable change........ ever!
We do not believe these things. We cannot believe these things.

Journal Entry: April 4, 1992

The day has been long. I am drowning in heaviness and grief. I cannot shake it. The culmination of all that I have heard this week pours in on my spirit. There is a heaviness I cannot throw over.
Tonight I am tired to the bone. I am exhausted. My spirit is broken. I am confronted by thoughts of Wendy when she is forty, and I am sixty-seven. Or fifty and I am seventy-seven. I know we cannot worry for the future but after this week of listening to the testimony of her deficits, the costs of future care for her, and all the compilations of those deficits which will mean that she will need trustees and others to help her, I think, but who will do it as lovingly as I? Will she have the best? No one cares, as we do. We spoil her mercilessly to lessen our pain at seeing her not have the things she used to have. How will she find what she needs when we are old, or frail, or ill, or gone?
I was so preoccupied and sorrowful that I totally forgot and missed my first class of teaching "Beginner Photographers" at the South West

Culture Centre..

The judge grants the application of a non-suit by Eigaard. A passenger in a vehicle has no responsibility to do anything. However the judge does require that Eigaard continue as a witness. I do not like Eigaard or Van Doorn. Eigaard is questioned and says, "I don't know," or, "I can't remember" to most of the questions. He claims not to remember the condition of the road, seeing the deer or Mrs. Stelter's car. He doesn't know when he got out of the car. Rob's cross-examination of him was a pleasure to watch, as Eigaard is made to look unbelievable, which he certainly is to me.

Rob says only two more witnesses remain. He says Eigaard will look like a good guy after they see Van Doorn, the man driving the car that originally hit the deer. Rob hammers at the fact that Van Doorn did nothing to alert any oncoming traffic, neglected to turn on his blinkers, did not even get out of the car to see where the deer was. He answers that he does not remember. He answers that he does not know. The trial is drawing to a close.

Wendy surprises us by going with Bruce to the Alberta Motor Vehicle Branch, to take her driver's test and gets her licence. First time! Hurray Wendy! Her seizure-free year is up! She was scheduled to go to the Glenrose for driver training the following week, but became impatient with all the waiting. When Bill says to Bruce, "Is this really true, Bruce? Did she really pass?" He says, "Dad, I've taken all these safety courses with Edmonton Telephones and she drives better than I do. Wendy's a really good driver."

The week flies by, and yet it feels as if we will never be done. The witnesses are all heard and gone. The tension stays. It is Thursday. We want to know the outcome, but we have planned a holiday at our little cabin in Parksville, on Vancouver Island. We booked 2 PM flights, as Rob was so sure it would be over by then, so we leave the courtroom at noon. The judge is still instructing the jury. We kiss Wendy goodbye, wish her well, and Bruce drives us to the airport. He goes back to the court house to find everyone at lunch in the noisy cafeteria in the basement. The jury is upstairs, sequestered, beginning their work.

Hours after our arrival, late that night, we learn from Bruce, as we stand in a telephone booth in the rain that the verdict of the jury is that Tom has no liability. Zero percent. Mrs. Stelter has 57 percent and Van Doorn, 43 percent. This means Wendy will get a second structured settlement from Van Doorn's insurance company. Bill and I are jubilant, but numb. We fall into bed. We try to sleep.

Next morning we wake at six. We decide to visit Tom's parents, even at seven in the morning, to tell them this great news. We drive to Qualicum Beach, five miles north of Parksville, and into their driveway. Ann comes to the door, wrapping herself in her dressing gown. Jim is just waking up.

We tell them the decision is in and there is no liability for Tom. None! They are thrilled. I cry with relief for five minutes. Ann puts the coffee on and we visit and have breakfast. We are good friends who have seen our dear childrens' lives wrecked with the accident. We share broken dreams, broken hearts, a great pain for them and for ourselves.

Journal Entry: April 20, 1992

We are still exhausted, but there is nothing to do except walk on the beach. We can just sit around and heal. Saturday I walked into a half-open door on my way to the bathroom and gave myself my first black eye.

Journal Entry: April 22, 1992

I don't know when we have ever been so exhausted. I am glad we made the effort to get here. Even putting film in the camera is a struggle. We saw a black bear on our way to the restaurant for supper. I made a couple of shots with my long lens, but it was too difficult.

Back in Edmonton, my life returns to normal. Wendy packs up her apartment because she is going to camp for the summer. We store her belongings. She drives up in her new truck! She went car shopping with Bruce while we were away and bought a shiny, black Toyota truck. Independent at last! She grins from ear to ear.

My job now is to put the house to rights and to prepare for the Winnipeg "New Beginnings" Brain Injury Conference, where Wendy and I are speaking together in ten days time.

Bob Mathewson, Judy Henderson and Ted Tremain agree to be trustees for Wendy to manage her structured settlements.

I go to the garden. The snow and ice are gone, the earth unfrozen. There are masses of yellow tulips bursting into bloom and tiny, purple crocuses out under the long living room window. The grass needs raking, the garden needs digging, and seeds must be planted. Feeling is coming back to the earth. Feeling is coming back in our lives. The trial of the trial is over.

Chapter 20

Camp Chief Hector

Wendy drives to Calgary for the first day in her first job since the accident. It is a volunteer job working with horses at Camp Chief Hector, a YMCA summer camp just outside Calgary. I have some concerns about not telling people at the Camp about Wendy's deficits. However she got the job on her own. I do not interfere. Bob said, when I was voicing these concerns, "Mum, they may never know." Boy, has he been out of touch for a long time!

Wendy and I go to a Winnipeg Brain Injury Conference and give a talk about being positive after brain injury. It is well received, but afterwards we both say that attending brain injury conferences can be very discouraging. The professionals say some very discouraging and negative things. But it feels good to work with Wendy on this project.

After the conference, Wendy returns to her job at Camp Chief Hector. Things aren't going very well there. She is unhappy and wonders where else she could go this summer. She phones us and talks of going to the States, coming here, going to the North Country Fair with Diane. I say, "Wendy, it won't be any better there. Running away won't help."

She celebrates her thirty-second birthday, struggling to know what she should do. Struggling every day. Struggling so hard.

Journal Entry: June 15, 1992. Saturday.

Ghost Dam, on my way home from camp, where Wendy is "horse staff."
The young wrangler, Wendy's boss, observed me watch Wendy saddle up a horse called Bingo and trot away on a trail ride. I must have looked concerned as he whispered quietly to me, "Don't worry about her, Mother." But I do. She has lost her sureness with the horses. As she bridled her horse, needing help, I remembered the confident eight-year old Wendy at Elkana Ranch, so many lifetimes ago.
They are doing a great job with her at Camp Chief Hector. The details and extent of her brain injury are incidental now and no one is interested. No one cares. It is just let's get on with the camp. They are, without knowing it, doing her vocational training. I guess it's time.
So amid a sodden sky and paddock, rain really raining, I left. I cannot let myself dwell on the Wendy I saw, so unsure of herself, looking to me for approval. She really hauled those wet bales of hay yesterday onto the wagon and carried the heavy harnesses from the stables for Prince and Duke, the two work horses.

Wendy comes home for some days off. We spend much of the time talking and talking, repeating the same old words. "No, you wouldn't be happier in the States, Wendy. Stay where you are. You can make this work. You have what you said you wanted. Horses, mountains, something to do." She goes over and over her options.

Journal Entry: July 5, 1992 Kananaskis.

Bill and I went with Wendy back to camp. We spoke to the two camp directors on Wendy's behalf, letting them know how she is feeling; that she isn't sure what she should do every day, she has no specific job or job description. What she is doing as a volunteer is not appreciated at all, no one seems to care that she is there. Bill and I go away thinking that speaking on her behalf has helped. They promise to rectify Wendy's concerns. .

Bill starts a new job. Wendy has her black Toyota truck stolen in Calgary and needs long-distance help in making a list of what she has lost. We take it down to the police station in Edmonton. They fax it to the Calgary Police Department.

Wendy phones again. She has twisted her back and is in great pain. She is alone at camp, trying to get bed rest in a teepee with no heat, no pain killers, no radio, no tapes and no friends. She called a Calgary friend for help but he has a full-time job.

We assist with the insurance claim, listing additional things Wendy has remembered being in her truck; a wet suit, her Daytimer, more clothes, her flute, and her new piccolo. More paperwork!

Wendy invites me to come to the camp to show the slide show about her recovery. She hasn't wanted me to show it for so long and now she is asking! I am delighted, and say I will go right away. I arrive, half way through Wendy's proposed four months at camp. She is sick with a chest infection. She has a low-grade fever and does not look well. There is no lustre in her eyes.

She takes me to the stables. She says her job is to capture the horses, bring them in and bridle and saddle them for the children's rides. She tells me the job is pretty hard for her because there are forty horses. Their bridles and saddles hang under their names in the barn. Because Wendy can't read or remember the horses names or understand directions when the head wrangler says, "Hey Wendy, head down to the corral there and get Midnight, Blackie and Old Paint, put the walking bridle on Blackie and saddle up the other two," she can't do her job right.

The head wrangler doesn't know that Wendy has to be shown what to do, not told. She hates telling anyone that she doesn't understand. So, rather than ask and ask again which horse is which, which tack belongs to each horse, she wanders out into the cold and rainy day, through the mud and manure of the corral, trying to catch a horse, any horse, hoping it will be the right one.

She hates needing special attention. She doesn't want to seem stupid. So she tries to do the job, even though she's confused most of the time.

Watching her try to do this job which would have been so easy for her once, is awful. I stand, leaning against the barn, sheltered from the rain and cold, feeling the scratch of the rough, grey boards on my back, watching her wander among the big horses, trying to catch one, hoping it's the right one, then bringing it back to the barn, wondering how to find someone to help her match the name on the tack. She is so courageous!

Other staff act as though she doesn't exist. They avoid eye contact with her, go about their work, but exclude her. She introduces me to everyone but we are of no significance. I realize that they think she is retarded! They are all eighteen and nineteen year olds. They couldn't care less about a young woman who doesn't keep up with the rest. They don't know she has had a brain injury or what that means. They don't know how smart she is and that once she could have been directing this stable and all it's activity. I watch, weeping in my heart for Wendy.

An unpleasant, petulant girl of seventeen, on crutches, moaning in her discomfort, calls out to Wendy to come over to where she is sitting. She directs Wendy to go over to that fence and bring her back her poncho. She does not even say "please." Wendy does as she is directed, brings back the poncho, gives it to the girl, who does not look at her or say "thank you." I am enraged. I am outraged. I cannot believe what I have seen.

I want to stride the twenty feet between us and shout at that girl, "What the hell do you think you are doing, ordering Wendy about like that? Don't you have the human decency to say "thank you" to someone who does something for you? Don't you know she has had a brain injury, and has to struggle with every word she says? Don't you know that she was in a coma for six weeks? Don't you know anything?"

And of course I don't. I ask myself how I can turn this into a positive learning experience. I realize I cannot go before Wendy for the rest of her life explaining her problems, her brain injury difficulties. She's on her own in the whole world. I can't go everywhere ahead of her to make sure people treat her with respect and worth; that they know she is a survivor of something so difficult that everyone should know how remarkable she is.

I stay where I am, heart rent with this realization. The strong lioness mother in me nullified. I can do nothing. I can only watch. I realize that her self-esteem is so low that she has not noticed this rudeness. I vow I will tell her what I have seen. I will tell her that she doesn't have to run errands for spoiled, rude people, that she has a right to ask for a "thank you", that she has great value and must respect herself. She deserves kindness and respect from others.

I watch the role she has created for herself for the rest of the afternoon. We meet more counsellors with whom Wendy is supposed to be working. They too, avoid her, make excuses for not including her in afternoon outings, for not having a place for her in the Red Cross swimming tests, and for excluding her from swimming. I fume.

That night I do what Wendy has asked me to do. I show the camp counsellors the slide show. They watch the progression from coma in intensive care, to hospital, to rehabilitation hospital, to her being home in her community and the end with the happy, hopeful day of her wedding to Tom.

Now, of course, Tom is gone. Couldn't take it. Couldn't watch the kind of thing I have been watching. I'm a little closer to understanding why.

The Camp staff gather around after the slide show and thank me for bringing it. They look at Wendy with new awareness. They value her a little bit more. They have a new respect for her. Wendy has given them something to think about. She is really smart to have thought of this.

I sleep in my van, Wendy in her tent. When morning comes Wendy comes to say goodbye. She thanks me for coming and I tell her how terrific she is and how well she is coping with these difficult days. We hug and say goodbye. I drive into the rising sun. I see a place where a small river tumbles from the mountains coursing deep into a crevasse in the rocks with a series of noisy waterfalls. There are worn places on the rocks beside the falls, where people over the years have come to sit.

I can hardly get out of the driver's seat fast enough. I have a well of tears flowing out of my eyes, a deep need to weep loudly, unrestrainedly, without fear of being overheard or comforted. To cry loudly, unchecked tears falling onto the ground, into this swirling noisy water, to be carried away by the angry water, swirling down the canyon. Anguish, agony, grief, and woe weep out of my eyes. Noise of my howling drowned out by the roar of the waterfalls. Nothing has prepared me for watching my daughter thought of as an imbecile.

And nothing has prepared me to conclude that there are some things I cannot do. I grieve as I try to accept that I cannot be everywhere Wendy is, that I must, as I did when she was little, allow her to find her own place in this world, without me.

After an hour it is over. I make myself some food and lie down in the van to rest. I meditate. I calm myself. I write in my journal.

Journal Entry: August 12, 1992

My beautiful daughter Wendy. Valueless! I cannot bear it. I would move these very mountains to change her life for her. But I cannot.

I have with me a book about my favourite author, May Sarton, called "Sarton Selected." One of her readers writes of caring for an old woman who was dying. She says; "I had to learn how to forgive myself for the many mistakes I made in trying to care for her in the ways that were best for her." These lines resonate for me.

Wendy broke my heart the other day when we went out for lunch in the middle of our shopping work to replace all the things she lost when her truck was stolen. She said that I never offer to buy lunch. That I only want to spend her money. She is paranoid now, that we only want to be with her for the money. Another problem to work through!

Wendy stays on at Camp Chief Hector and finishes her commitment to them. It is a tough few weeks but she does it! She particularly enjoys working with children with hearing impairments who come out for a special week. She feels she has much in common with them. The staff are more understanding of Wendy's difficulties now. I am relieved, and very proud of her for recognizing that they needed to see the slide show and for asking me to come to show it.

As President of NABIS, I put in many hours of volunteer time for the organization. Wendy feels that I am self aggrandizing. That I am making a career of her brain injury. That I am important because of her disability.

I am wounded by her accusations and suspicions. It hurts me deeply to be thought to be taking advantage of her situation. I look carefully at myself and my motivation. Could she be right? It is possible that she is. I do enjoy leadership. I enjoy public speaking. I enjoy organizing. But I do not wish to cause her more pain.

We go around and around with this issue. I say I will resign if she asks me to. I am not trying to hurt her. I am not wanting to be in the

the spotlight if this is causing her more pain. I try to explain that I can help the organization grow, I have talents which will help NABIS help other people affected by brain injury. I have time to give.

I come to the conclusion that she may never understand.

Bill supports whatever decision I make. I decide to stay on as president. Each issue of our newsletter has a president's message. Almost five years after Wendy's accident, in September 1992, I write this message:

President's Message

As many of you know, Traumatic Brain Injury catapulted into our lives almost five years ago. Our daughter, Wendy's skull was smashed into her brain in a car accident. An all-too-common theme.

She has had a remarkable recovery. Friends often say, " Aren't you lucky! Wendy is doing so well!"

This is true. There are those whose lives are not so blessed. However I need to let those people know a little more about what "doing so well" means.

It means waking alone, when before she had a love.
It means having no job, when before she had many.
It means having few friends, when before she had dozens.
It means having self doubts, when before she had few.
It means being excluded, when before she was sought.
It means being dependent, when before she was depended upon.
It means crying a lot, when before she was known for her smile.
It means having no purpose, when before she was ideal driven.
It means enduring a life, when before life was for living.

This is terribly painful to live. It is painful for us, her parents, to see. I feel self-indulgent when I say how hard it is for me, her mother, to watch her daily trials.

But Wendy is remarkably wise. She recently told me that I must change my attitude. I need to let go of "before."
I think she is right. I do.
"Before" is now irrelevant.
What is relevant is that her life is incredibly hard.

Even five years after the accident, I need help in letting go of "before". I am not alone. Hundreds of parents, spouses, children and loved ones affected by traumatic brain injury need support in learning to live with the "now".

NABIS is providing that support.

Wendy gets a nice black lab dog called Licorice from the SPCA. He is a good companion. The dog will alleviate some of her loneliness. She goes on a camping trip with him into the mountains. She winds her way from Jasper, south to her friend Judy Henderson in Medicine Hat. Judy is feeding the baby and the dog bites the baby. Wendy has the dog put down by the SPCA when she gets back to Edmonton.

Chapter 21

Back to Calgary

Wendy decides to live in Calgary to continue at the Reading Foundation. She still wants to be away from us. Steve Truch thinks that Wendy will do well this year as she is more motivated. She commits to six more months. She buys another dog from the SPCA and puts an ad in the paper for "Shared Accommodation". Her requirements for wanting a house are incredibly restrictive. A large, airy house with dog, smoking, recreation-minded people, and mostly men. She is really looking for a boyfriend as well! She finds a place with four other people and moves in.

Soon she realizes that these people with whom she is living are taking advantage of her. They borrow her car, eat the groceries she buys for herself, and abuse her generous nature. She decides to find an apartment for herself. She has help from Zane Berezuk, an old friend of Tom's who is very fond of Wendy, and Jackie and Lyle Ford, parents of Wendy's friend, Lee-Anne Walker. She stays with the Fords in a mountain-facing home west of Calgary, and they treat her just like a daughter. She finds a nice apartment on Elbow Drive. Her new dog runs away and is very strange. The Fords suggest that the dog be put down.

Wendy is finally living by herself. She is pleased with this arrangement. Mid-January I go to Calgary to visit. Wendy has asked me to help with her money matters. I love being in my daughter's apartment. She makes me welcome. She has a nice hard bed for me to sleep on, a generous dining room table and her kitchen is stocked with things I know from my own cupboards.

Journal Entry: January 22, 1993
Calgary 8948 Elbow Drive. Apt 319
I am in Wendy's nice, sunny apartment on a beautiful day. It is special to be in a daughter's apartment. Daughters learn how to make a house a home from their mothers, and I feel really comfortable here.

Journal Entry: January 23, 1993, Red Deer
I went to Calgary to get Wendy's money matters in order. I let it go until now, having made excuses that because there were no rent or food costs at the Y Camp and then at the Fords and then at the house with the undesirables, it was not necessary. Now finally she is settled but still wants to be a nomad with no roots.
I found the lack of little side tables for lamps or magazines difficult. Everything was on the floor. Because it is hard for me to bend, I went to a liquidators special, bought an end table and coffee table for $79.95 and then saw two more end tables and a coffee table for $99.95 so I bought both sets because Wendy needs bedside tables too. I thought she could sell the extra coffee table and still be ahead.
It looks better now, but Wendy keeps saying she wants to move and so does not want to accumulate furniture. She wants to work in Banff or somewhere else. She doesn't want to burden herself with more belongings.
I feel that to be settled somewhere, having a known rent, a known bank and a familiar neighbourhood is going to help her feel more stable. I

think these things could bring some constancy to her life. The
structured settlements give her a fair amount of money per month, but
she thinks she is spending more than that. We need to get a handle on
what she is spending. She still is unhappy that I need to help her.
I put it off in November because she lost her purse and her cheque book
twice, plus she had her truck and contents stolen in the summer, which
did muddle things. Now to put some order here.

Wendy joins a band in Calgary and, through the band, finds a
boy friend, Ray. He is a stout, pleasant man who is a cook. He doesn't
move in with Wendy but is around a lot and makes good meals. We
meet him when they both come up to Edmonton to get Wendy's
computer. Ray seems very agreeable, a nice companion for Wendy. I
am happy that he will alleviate her loneliness.

Journal Entry: March 14, 1993

I had a good day yesterday. Breakfast with Wendy in Calgary and then
a visit to our dear friends, Bill and Franny Hall. I said I was worried
about Wendy being so dozy. Bill, a physician, said, "Who is medically
monitoring her seizure medication?" "No one," I said, suddenly aware
that I have let this slip. He said he would have her checked on Monday
at noon. God! How could I have forgotten about blood levels?
Last evening, I met with a friend to plan a five-night, six-day
photography workshop in the mountains called "Wild Flowers and
Waterfalls". Wendy wanted to be included somehow in this endeavour
to get back to her Uneek Experience trips. As we met, it became
obvious that Wendy was unable to do any of the tasks in planning this
venture. She cannot notify the journals and magazines for the publicity,
she cannot prepare the brochure, she cannot make reservations, she
cannot even phone people to tell them about it. It becomes apparent
how difficult it is for her to contribute and how hard it is for us to find

something real in which to include her.

Wendy decides it is time to go to the Head Injury Relearning Centre in Calgary, (HIRC). They accept her but she is angry that they need to do another assessment. She feels she has been assessed far too many times in the past five years. She does not want to do it like everyone else but in half the time.

Wendy is lonely a great deal of the time. She is invited out to a party by one of the teachers she likes at the Reading Foundation. She leaves home but spends more than an hour trying to find the address. She gets lost and then becomes impatient and goes home, feeling desolate and angry with herself for not being able to figure out how to get where she wants to go.

My workshop trip of Wildflowers and Waterfalls begins at Cathedral Mountain Chalet in Field, BC. I stay with Wendy on my way to the mountains and invite her to join us if she wishes. Disaster strikes, when we look at the first slides we get back from the local processor. All are ruined. We can hardly use any of them for teaching. Our students are already dealing with the worst week of rain in the mountains in years. Then Wendy turns up and we ask her to courier our film into Calgary. She does for the rest of the week. We are saved by Wendy! I am very proud of her, and she feels good to have been able to contribute.

Chapter 22

The Sixth Year

Wendy decides that she does not want to continue with the HIRC in Calgary. She feels that they treat her like a patient and she is tired of being a patient. I think she is right. She has learned a little from HIRC but when she learned that they didn't want her to drive her worker to her house, and wanted Wendy to take the bus, it was the last straw. She withdraws from the program, with our support. There are some very real put-downs which belittle people attending brain injury programs.

Wendy is beginning to accept that she has a larger support system in Edmonton. She has parents, brothers, old friends and acquaintances here, and she needs us all. She knows the layout of the city better and doesn't get lost here. She is relaxing about needing our help a little bit, so she moves back to Edmonton.

Barb and Dwight York, old friends of Wendy's, help her move and settle into a house, not far from us, where a young man rents out rooms. Getting organized has never been what Wendy does best, so we help her arrange her belongings into a house.

For a holiday, Wendy flies to Whitehorse, in the Yukon, to stay with her brother Bob, and his wife Shelley, before she goes on a great

Tatshenshini River raft trip. Wendy is quite ill with another chest infection, so she rests with Bob and Shelley for a few days before the trip. It is a very popular and highly priced trip. She is unwell when she begins and is cold and very miserable the first night. She feels that she can hardly set up her own tent. She asks a man if she can share his tent. He is greatly offended, misunderstanding her motives as it is difficult for her to explain that she is ill. All she wants is to have someone else set up the tent and some extra warmth, but trying to explain this to someone who does not know why she speaks strangely obviously didn't quite work. The trip is a lonely experience for her and she says she will never do one again alone. She returns to Edmonton.

Journal Entry: August 30, 1993
Wendy was here yesterday morning and I got very angry with her about her drinking. I feel so intolerant!

Wendy's speaking and comprehension get incredibly slower if she has been drinking even a little the day before. I am impatient when I realize, having repeated myself several times about something, that she probably had alcohol the night before. When I ask, I feel like I am treating her like a teenager. I hate that, and she does too, but I still respond badly, with no compassion or gentleness. I am condemning and blaming. Wendy is never drunk but just slowed down, and I am impatient.

Wendy decides that she will try Rebuilding, a new program at the Edmonton Brain Injury Relearning Society. They have enough staff to spend the required time with each client. The program uses resources in the community to help people find work. She will volunteer in a job, while being supervised by a Rebuilding worker. Then she will be evaluated and possibly find employment.

The family has to be very much involved. Wendy's worker is a psychologist, Corinne Thorsell, a friendly, warm person who used to work at NABIS. She is a good choice. She is patient and thorough, going over everything painstakingly. She does a home visit to Wendy's house. She meets with family members. She organizes pages of expectations for those who are involved in Wendy's life. It is very detailed and focuses on what it is Wendy wants to do.

Wendy's job experience is at the Edmonton YMCA in their Day Care Centre. She does child care. Wendy doesn't like it much and is impatient with being supervised.

Journal Entry: November 30, 1993

Today is the anniversary date of Wendy's accident. Yesterday at Toastmasters, I was supposed to talk about Structured Settlements with another member. He did his talk and then I tried to do mine but I was openly in tears at the beginning. I managed to talk and show slides for 10 minutes. I had another member in tears by the time I was done.

I was a wreck for the rest of the afternoon! I just made myself walk and I made supper but I felt very heavy all evening, totally unable to do anything constructive. Sweet Bill said, "What can I do to help? Can I give you a massage or something?" so I said, "No, just hold me, the way we used to cuddle on the chesterfield at my house before we were married, for hours, watching the fire." So he held me and we talked about the last six years.

Now, I cannot remember Wendy before her accident or what she was like. I have lost that daughter. I cannot remember her. She looks the same but is different. I am mourning the old Wendy tonight. It is a great loss, but it is one more step in accepting the new Wendy.

Wendy puts her skis through the rear window of her Toyota. Impulsively, she decides to buy a new one. She asks Bill to help her deal, so that she is not taken advantage of. Good thinking. Bill has laryngitis and a cold today and should stay warm in bed, but goes out to help Wendy buy a car.

Last week, Wendy's Toyota slid on black ice into another car on 122 Street. For some reason the woman whose car she hit phoned me and Bill. More ongoing crises, but at least we are in the same city as Wendy. She doesn't do these things on purpose. She more than tries her best, but it must be said, these episodes take their toll on us. I feel our grandchildren do not see as much of us as they might, but I am sure Bruce and Michele understand. A tiny part of me resents the time we spend with Wendy's crises, and then I feel guilty.

Now Wendy's housemate calls us. He is a bit of a fusspot, and is distraught at some of the things Wendy does. She leaves the fridge door open. She puts the wrong detergent in the dishwasher, causing it to overflow. She puts a heavy jacket in the washing machine, causing it to unbalance and stop working. He phones us wondering what to do.

Wendy is fed up trying to live with others. She phones a friend in real estate. Together they find a house for Wendy to buy. No more landlords, no more roommates, no more complaints about her habits. She settles into her own house.

Wendy's life smooths out. She has fewer lost wallets, missed dates and emergencies. She is happier, smiles more, connects with more friends, joins a local band. She is busy and beginning to enjoy herself.

Chapter 23
Independence

Wendy now lives in her own little house about ten minutes drive from us in Edmonton. Her neighbours are friendly and pleasant. There are two small girls who often come and play with her dog. A delightful, elderly woman across the lane, a fabulous gardener, watches Wendy's house like a good neighbour should.

Wendy bought a dog the same week she bought her house. Kurly-Sue is a spirited, frisky, amber-eyed, chocolate brown, curly haired Chesapeake Retriever. She is a puppy who adores Wendy. Wen remembers that in her Recreation Therapy job, years before, she read about pets alleviating loneliness, that people living alone with pets are healthier than those without pets. Wendy now has her own reasons for having Kurly-Sue. She has companionship, walks, and is greeted warmly with unlimited amounts of tail wagging, when she comes home.

Her house has an L-shaped living-dining room, hardwood floors and a smallish kitchen. There is a good-sized back yard for the dog. One of the first things Wendy buys is a barbecue so she can have her friends and family over for meals.

I offer to make drapes for her nine-foot, west-facing, living room window. There are yards of delicate pink, green and blue flowered chintz on my extended dining room table. Wendy and I have fun choosing fabric together. I have not made curtains since Bill and I moved into our first new house in Calgary in 1959, so I am very careful. Wendy was never a seamstress. She does not easily visualize what the finished product will be like. It feels really good to work with my daughter on her house.

I go to the graduation exercises of Kurly-Sue from puppy school. I interrupt the class, taking pictures to record this special event. Wendy is glad to see me, but the instructor is not. I distract Kurly-Sue so that she pays attention to me, not to Wendy. Kurly-Sue does not do as well as she could have, but Wendy doesn't seem to mind.

Later, at Wendy's, I try the lamp shade Bill and I bought at a sale. It isn't the right size for the lamp. Wendy disappears into her bedroom, puts the new shade on another lamp, takes the brown bedroom shade and puts it on the lamp in the living room. Now everything looks terrific. Hurray, another detail taken care of in the many that need attention when moving.

We hug goodnight and I congratulate Kurly-Sue on her graduation as I leave. "Why don't you come over for breakfast, Wen?" I ask. "Friends from Saskatoon are here and we will be having breakfast about 8:30."

"Great," she says.

Next morning she's up at 6:30 AM, meets her walking buddies with Kurly-Sue on their regular morning route. Then her red truck pulls up to our house at 8:30 AM. She tells us it has taken her twenty minutes to travel the usual seven-minute trip. The traffic is crawling on new snow over glassy ice.

I have hot bran muffins just out of the oven. Wendy thinks hot bran muffins are not a real breakfast worth travelling across town for on a cold, slippery morning. She's hungry. Everyone agrees that eggs would be a nice treat. I scramble golden eggs while Wendy makes toast and finds some great jam which I have forgotten is in the cupboard.

We sit, chatting and catching up. Wendy is a terrific hostess, making more toast, passing the tea, and remembering to look after people. She is good about thinking of others and seeing to their needs. She always clears up too, loading the dishwasher and cleaning the kitchen.

She is going over to Parkview Elementary school to work as a volunteer in the library. They have recently told her she could work with some of the children for whom English is not a first language. I know nothing of this new work of hers and wonder once again at her indomitable spirit, finding ways to be useful in her community.

She volunteers at the John Janzen Nature Centre, in the river valley, where she assists the naturalists in the outdoor walks and activities. She volunteers at the Disabled Skiers program. Last year Wendy assisted a blind woman, picking her up, driving her home, and skiing with her. In the summer, she volunteers with the Parks and Recreation program so that she is outdoors as much as possible. As well, she volunteers with Hole's Greenhouse in St. Albert, a suburb of Edmonton, assisting Lois Hole in her presentations.

I too, volunteer. I continue my work with NABIS. The organization is growing and my personal goal of creating a strong board has been met. NABIS moves into new quarters, near the Glenrose Hospital. The name of NABIS is becoming better known in our community.

I become a board member of the Hope Foundation, an organization dedicated to the study and encouragement of hope. My connections to other photographers enable me to gather a stunning collection of images from various photographers across Canada. We call it "Images of Hope". We acquire funds from a private donor to frame the collection and have a gala opening at a local prestigious art gallery.

Bill has found a super job as Executive Director of the Edmonton Community Foundation. He is involved in raising funds and managing the day-to-day activities of the foundation.

On November 11, we attend a concert at the Jubilee Auditorium for Remembrance Day. It is an event put on by the Cosmopolitan Music Society. Wendy has been playing flute with them since she moved back to Edmonton. She has also been taking private flute lessons to increase her skills. She sits in the second row, looking perfect, her lovely, blond hair pulled back in a French braid. She is wearing the required black skirt and a snowy white blouse. She holds her flute out to the side, just as we have watched her do since she was thirteen and first played in her junior high school band.

I am so proud of her sitting up there playing stirring band marches, while all the old men, and some women veterans in the audience stand as their regimental march is played. I think about my father, who would be eighty-nine now if he were alive. He died eleven days before Wendy was born. I remember Mum saying that it often happens: someone dies and a baby is born soon afterwards who helps take the place of the person who is gone, completing the circle of life.

Dad is very much with me this evening. He stands beside me, bald, tall, with his shoulders smartly back, smelling of after shave and Listerine, chest full of the military medals he was awarded in the years between 1939 and 1945. Just like all the other veterans behind and beside us, he stands proud.

I silently say to him, "Look Dad. Look at Wendy. Hasn't she done well? You know, Dad, don't you, all that she's been through? You know how difficult life is for her now, every day, don't you, Dad? And here she is sitting up on the stage playing the music you loved, the music we shared in the war years. Aren't you amazed at how well she is doing, after what she has been through?"

They play, "There'll Be Blue Birds Over The White Cliffs Of Dover." That song was our family's song. The words, "Jimmy will go to sleep in his own little room again," made it our song. Jimmy is my older brother. When Dad's regiment was stationed all over the country, we moved time after time so that we could be near him and so that he could be with us when he was on leave. All of us wanted to get back to our own little room again.

Tonight, in this large auditorium, up on the lighted stage, Wendy plays to honour the veterans. "To honour you, Dad, and the part you played keeping Canada safe in World War ll. Dammit, Dad, I wish you could be here to see this wondrous thing, to see Wendy sitting here with this band on the stage of the Jubilee Auditorium, playing her flute."

He is proud of Wendy too, and stands at rigid attention with me when she plays "God Save The Queen," and "O Canada."

Bill and I watch our daughter together. She comes to the edge of the stage when it is over.

"Well done, Wendy. Well done," we say.

"Thanks, Mum and Dad. Thanks for coming."

Bill and I drive home to our house and Wendy drives herself home to Kurly-Sue and her own life.

Journal Entry: November 12, 1993

At the Jubilee Auditorium last night Wendy was fabulous on the stage, in the band. It felt as though we were getting back to normal at last. She looked lovely and was smiling and chatting to her many friends in the band.

I am busy these days teaching photography, shooting slides for stock sales and editing the newsletter for the camera club. The "Images of Hope" project is growing and the University of Alberta has given the Hope Foundation a house on campus. This is a great leap forward.

NABIS has raised enough money to hire a part-time volunteer co-ordinator. Life is pretty good right now.

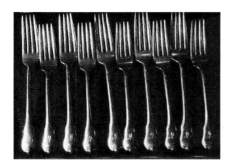

Chapter 24

The Dinner Party

It is a cold, grey day and a light snow dusts the ground. I am arranging pink roses and baby's breath. A bouquet for the centre of a table. Wendy's table. She is having a dinner party tonight. It is the seventh anniversary of her accident. The invited guests are her lawyers and their spouses, Bill and me.

Wendy and her Dad have been busy preparing a goose and two ducks which they shot this fall, on a hunting trip in northern Alberta.

I take the flowers over to her house in the afternoon. Wendy is at a flute lesson. The house is spotless. The kitchen window is open and it smells fresh and airy. The new chintz curtains in the living room match the colours of the chesterfield. There are green plants around the room and candles on the table. It is set with a white linen cloth and her good cutlery. Her groceries are there, still in their bags. I unpack broccoli, cauliflower, lettuce, paper napkins and whipping cream for the pumpkin pie. I arrange a few things, put the fresh vegetables in the fridge and sit waiting to turn the oven on. Possibly Wendy will be kept at her lesson and I want to put the roasting pan in on time.

Wendy arrives home with Kurly-Sue. She thanks me for my help and goes through a last-minute check of what's to be done before the guests arrive at six.

I go home to rest and put my feet up. I think about the long journey we have made since that black night, seven years ago. I remember the coma, the days in intensive care, rehabilitation, the days after discharge when none of us knew what to do. I remember Wendy's seizures, her anger and her bewilderment after Tom left. I contemplate the tears and the pain of all those years but also of the strengths we acquired, the good people who have stood by us and I realize how far we have come. I think of Wendy's indomitable spirit and the number of people she inspires by her tenacity and persistence as she carries on, doing what all of us do, seeking meaning in our lives.

I think of some of the lessons I have learned:

To pay attention to my gut.

To act on my intuition.

To honour the psychic connections between people.

To ask for help when I need it.

To accept help when it is offered.

I have learned that I am unable to go before my children, explaining their difficulties to the world, to pave the way for them, nor do they want me to. I have learned that somehow the universe gives me what I need when I need it. I remember back to the story of perspective that I heard so long ago; that the two divergent views, the medical view of prognosis and the family's view of the future meet in the distance of time. I think this is so.

I have learned that a family can expand to include the people who stay close and involved. And, I have learned to never underestimate the power of a family.

I have also learned practical ways of easing the difficulties for families after brain injury. Some of them are:

Educate yourself. Get all the information you can handle as soon as you can. It will allow you to ask better questions of the individuals caring for your loved one.

Know that you are a medical consumer with a right to know. Staff in the hospital are there for you. Believe you have a right to ask any questions you need to. Do not feel that you are "bothering" the staff or the physician. It is their responsibility to inform you.

Take your cues about what to do next from the person with the brain injury when you can.

Use the telephone answering machine to bring good news from friends, and to let them keep in touch without bothering you. It also lets you update callers on the injured person's progress.

Have a gathering of family and friends or a ceremony of hope. Gather together to share concern, to be intentional about hope, and to focus on a positive outcome in order to find strength to face the days ahead and to create collective energy.

Have a collage of photographs hanging on the hospital wall that people can add to which will assist with speech problems that might arise. It is also a great keepsake for the person once out of the coma.

Know that it's all right to take breaks. In order to be a good caregiver, you must be well, so care for your own health during this process. If that means having counselling, taking a weekend off, or leaving for a while, do it, so you can come back with renewed effectiveness.

Believe that you will never be sent more than you can handle.

Seek out local brain injury associations. The people you meet there have experienced similar situations and will support you. They will answer your questions and often have good ideas of what is available in the community after discharge from the active treatment hospital. They will also accept you as you are and understand the journey you are on.

Accept your own feelings of anger, frustration, and despair.

Forgive yourself for feeling that way.

Believe in miracles.

Respond to feelings. Listen beyond and deeper than the words coming from the person healing from the brain injury. Ask how they feel.

Keep good records in preparation for a legal case. The lawyers need details of the money you spend, expenses you incur because of the accident, and a chronology of when things happen. Keep names and job descriptions of the people who treat the person with the brain injury.

Record when new skills and behaviours happen because it's good to look back on where you were, when you think there is no progress.

Visualize what you need.

Explore all the options for financial support for treatment: government departments, Alberta Motor Vehicles Accident Claims Branch, Assured Income for the Severely Handicapped, community groups, foundations, scholarships and service clubs, or similar agencies in your area which might have bonus programs for extra needs, for aids to daily living, for rent subsidies, and for special housing.

Check with your social worker or brain injury associations for information on financial assistance. Tell them what you need.

Know that people with brain injuries keep on learning, just as the rest of us do throughout our lives.

It has indeed been a long journey. I continue to rest and think of today's Wendy with the winning smile who has met a thousand challenges since her accident. I think of how grateful I am that I still have my daughter. Wendy says again and again, when she speaks of her difficulties, "It just takes time," she says, "It just takes time!"

She is right. It just takes time.

I remember that Diane said, at the positive prayer service the first week after the accident, Wendy has a special job to do now. She spreads sunshine and hope. People are glad to see Wendy as she brightens a room with her smile. She is funny. She is honest. She is always game to try something new, ready to join in whatever is going on and to organize recreational events. She has opened new pathways in her brain for all this learning. She has leaped many hurdles. I am full of admiration.

I think, as I lie on my bed resting, it is quite remarkable that we are going out for dinner tonight at Wendy's house.

Bill comes home. We dress and drive over to arrive a few minutes before six. All is ready. We carry in extra plates, a large platter and some extra glasses. The house smells wonderfully of roasting wild goose and steaming vegetables. Wendy, in an apron, greets us with her wonderful smile and asks us to put our coats in the bedroom. She is giving Rob and Brandy Graesser a tour of the house. They are delighted to see her doing so well. They genuinely care about Wendy. Bill Barclay and Mavis Booker arrive. Wendy helps everyone pour drinks in the kitchen and suggests we move into the living room where she's left hors d'oeuvres on her gleaming, new, glass coffee table.

To our surprise, we see an empty plate and a very satisfied looking Kurly-Sue. She has never seen a plate of special treats put just at muzzle level before, but she hasn't waited for an invitation to gulp down the crackers and cheese, celery and olives. We all have a great laugh and a better appetite for the meal to come.

Toasts are made to Wendy, to her incredible recovery, her words, her speaking abilities and to her good health. We sit around the table, while Bill carves the goose and Wendy serves the wild rice and broccoli. There is wine for those who wish it and soft drinks for others. There is a delicious orange pumpkin pie for dessert. Conversation flourishes. We move to the living room for coffee.

The doorbell rings. Bruce, Michele, Kyle, Kory and Keyfer, our newest grandson, come in to say hello. There is much chatter with more congratulations for Wendy and all she has accomplished. She accepts the praise with tears of gratitude in her eyes and responds in fun.

It is a week night so, reluctantly, people leave, thanking Wendy for the lovely dinner and the delightful evening. How charming this was. We go home. How extraordinary, the ordinary.

Postscript

By Wendy,
in conversation with her
friend, Katie Walker

November, 1995

It has been eight years since the accident. I've heard that if you were in a coma, it will take you one year for every week to recover. I was in a coma for six weeks so that is six years. Then it takes another two years for your heart to get better. So I figure that this is my eighth year since the accident, and it is time to move on.

I have a feeling I was in a dream for two months. The first thing I remember was seeing this guy. Tom. Cute. He helped me physically. He even bought me a bug, a Volkswagen. That was a year and a half after the accident. I never wanted to try driving. The car was too low. He kept trying but he didn't stay. That's why the heart hurts and your anger of what you are doing. Why I am here.

The doctors would say, after this time, you won't be able to do it this way. I'm real positive that my folks and family never let me stop trying and I think they better keep doing that. Don't say after two years, she won't be able to do it that way. And so that is why Tom left. They kept saying, "Oh well."

Now I am getting more aware that people have the same problems. That is why I'm becoming more aware of people rather than myself. I've been by myself for a long time and that is sort of sad.

When you are living with someone you are talking more. You are doing things. Physically you're actually talking properly. It makes it hard. I suppose you can enjoy it.

I've been by myself. Maybe I've just sort of grown up. After the third year, I just said, I've got to get away from my family so I left and went to Calgary. I did about a year and a half trying to get better. Then I thought I'd like to come back where people knew me. In Calgary they'd say, "Oh, she's weird. She's brain injured."

I'm going to have a date. He doesn't know about me. Now I think I have to be fun and just smile. I must have to get away from the last eight years. I have to say, "Look at those roses."

That is why it took a long time for me. I guess men are different from women. I'm not really sure how they are different. I have three brothers. I'm more used to guys. I like their company more than women. I've had to get more involved with women because they care more. It's interesting. I am more involved with people, mostly other women. Most of the people I saw at the hospital were women. The reason I like the speech therapist is he was a man.

I was a recreational therapist. I have had to become my own recreational therapist. I get bored so I keep busy. It makes me feel better about myself. I'm enjoying myself when I feel like I'm my own person.

I did the West Coast Trail on the west side of Vancouver Island about three years after the accident. I went with my friend May. All I remember is walking, walking, walking. I'd get there and sleep.

My friend wanted Mum and me to speak. I guess it was my impression that I'd already told Mum that I didn't want to show the slides about the accident. There were pictures at the hospital. I didn't think the slide show would be there. The slides were there. I talked. Then Mum talked. It was everything about me. I want to do something fun. I don't want to think about the accident all the time. I'm not going to talk about the injury anymore. I know it is important for others. I've been doing it for Mum. Tom couldn't handle it anymore either.

I don't want to read the book. I just want to say that don't plan to get back to what you used to do. Focus on your abilities now. I don't want to hang around head injured people. I'm lucky. I've got a second try at what I'm going to do for the rest of my life. I'd like to get back to where I was in terms of fun and I'd like to enjoy today. Do what you want to do.

Organizations in Alberta for people affected by brain injury

Northern Alberta Brain Injury Society (NABIS)   Tel (780) 479-1757
229 Royal Alex Place   Fax (780) 474-4415
Edmonton, Alberta T5G 0B4   Email: nabis@abihelp.org

Central Alberta Brain Injury Society (CABIS)   Tel (403) 341-3463
#18 4712 Ross Street   Fax (403) 346-1035
Red Deer, Alberta T4N 1X2   Email: cabrain@incentre.net

Southern Alberta Brain Injury Society (SABIS)   Tel (403) 521-5212
Suite 137 2723 37 Ave S.E.   Fax (403) 283-5867
Calgary, Alberta T1Y 5R8   Email: sabis@sabis.ab.ca
                                                   Web: www.sabis.ab.ca

Lloydminster and Area Brain Injury Society (LABIS) Tel (306) 825-7212
#3 4620-44 Street   Fax (306) 825-7213
Lloydminster, SK S9V 0G4   Email: labis@sasknet.com

Programs in Alberta

Edmonton Brain Injury Relearning Society (EBIRS)   Tel (780) 477-7575
#311 10106-111 Ave   Fax (780) 471-4288
Edmonton, Alberta T5G 0B4   Email: info@ ebirs.ab.ca
                                                   Web: www.ebirs.ab.ca

Association For the Rehabiliatation of the Brain Injured Tel (403) 242-7116
3412 Spruce Drive, SW   Fax (403) 242-7478
Calgary, Alberta T3C 3A4   Email: info@ arbi.ca
                                                   Web: www.arbi.ca

Brain Injury Rehabilitation Centre   Tel (403) 297-0100
#300 815-8 Ave   Fax (403) 234-8860
Calgary, Alberta T2P 3P2   Email: birc@brainrehab.ca
                                                   Web: www.brainrehab.ca

Principal Canadian Organization

Brain Injury Association of Canada   Tel (418) 529-9990
574 Boulevard Des Capucins   Fax (418) 524-7333
Quebec City, PQ G1J 3R8   Email: info@raptccq.com

Principal Provincial Organizations

Newfoundland and Labrador Brain Injury Association   Tel (709) 579-3070
220 Lemarchant Road, Suite 306   Fax (709) 579-3109
St. John's NF A1C 2H8   Email: nbia@nsnibn.com
   Web: www.nbia.nf.ca

Brain Injury Association of Nova Scotia   Tel (902) 473-7301
PO Box 8804   Fax (902) 473-7302
Halifax, NS B3K 5M4   Email: bians1@ns.sympatico.ca
   Web: www.ns.simpatico.ca/bians1

Brain Injury Association of New Brunswick   Tel (506) 454-9537
527 Beaverbrook Court
Fredericton, NB E3B 1X6

Association Québécoise des Traumatisés Craniens   Tel (514) 274-7447
911 Jean Talon, Est   Fax (514) 274-1717
Montréal, PQ L2R 1V5   Email: aqtc@aqtc.ca

Ontario Brain Injury Association   Tel (905) 641-8877
PO Box 2338   Fax (905) 641-0323
St. Catherines, ON L2R 7R9   Email: obia@ obia.on.ca
   Web: www.obia.on.ca

Manitoba Brain Injury Association Inc.   Tel (204) 953-5353
#204 825 Sherbrook Street   Fax (204) 975-3027
Winnipeg, MB R3A 1M5   Email: mbia@mts.net
   Web : www.mbia.ca

Saskatchewan Brain Injury Association   Tel (306) 373-1555
230 Avenue R South, 1702-20 Street West   Fax (306) 373-5655
Saskatoon, SK S7M 0Z9   Email: info_sbia@sasktel.net
   Web: www.braininjury-sbia.ca

Lower Mainland Brain Injury Association   Tel (604) 521-0833
209-88 Tenth Street   Fax (604) 521-9141
New Westminster, BC V3M 6H8   Email: 1mbia_CO@telus.net
   Web: 1mbia.org

Principal United States Organization

Brain Injury Association of America   Tel (703) 761-0750
8201 Greenboro Drive, Suite 611   Fax (703) 761-0755
McLean, VA 22102   Web: www.biausa.org

Updated December 2003

About the Author

Mufty Mathewson, BPT, physical and occupational therapist, teacher, and photographer lives in Edmonton with her husband Bill. They have four children and three grandsons.

Mufty has taught at McGill University, at the University of Alberta, and at the City Arts Centre.

Mufty has published many articles on rehabilitation and photography. She has had several one-woman photographic art shows, and markets her photography through Photo Search Ltd., in Edmonton.

Her passion is making photo-essays on psychosocial issues. The best known of her projects are "Raising Kids is Hard: When You're Alone, It's Harder," "Look Beyond" (award winner in International Year of Disabled Persons), and "Health and Healing in Photography."

She is past president of the Northern Alberta Brain Injury Society, of Images Alberta Camera Club, and serves on the board of the HOPE Foundation in Edmonton.

Courage After Coma: A Family's Journey
by Mufty Mathewson

Discover how a family overcame a serious brain injury. A gripping story told by a mother who fought to keep her family together.

This book can be ordered from:
Uneek Experience Ltd.
10333 132 Street,
Edmonton, Alberta, Canada T5N 1Y9

ISBN 0-9682221-0-2
Tel/Fax (780) 452-6224
Email: muftynbill@shaw.ca

Enclosed is my cheque/moneyorder to purchase _____ copies of *Courage After Coma.*

Name: _____

Address: _____ Apt.: _____

City: _____ Province/State: _____

Postal Code/Zip Code _____

Price: **$20.00 + $4.00** shipping and handling per copy, + an extra $.50 shipping and handling for each additional copy. Canadian funds.

Books shipped upon receipt of payment.

Please make cheque payable to: <u>**Mathewson**</u>

A percentage of the sale of this book will be donated to the Northern Alberta Brain Injury Society.